RC
460
J3

D1105881

MYTHS OF MADNESS

Myths of Madness

NEW FACTS

FOR OLD FALLACIES

Don D. Jackson, M.D.

The Macmillan Company, New York

Collier-Macmillan Limited, London

Copyright © DON D. JACKSON 1964

All rights reserved—no part of this book may be reproduced in any form without permission in writing from the publisher, except by a reviewer who wishes to quote brief passages in connection with a review written for inclusion in magazine or newspaper.

First Printing

Printed in the United States of America

The Macmillan Company, New York
Collier-Macmillan Canada, Ltd., Toronto, Ontario

Library of Congress catalog card number: 64-12536

DESIGNED BY RONALD FARBER

To My Family

D. HIDEN RAMSEY LIBRARY
ASHEVILLE-BILTMORE COLLEGE
ASHEVILLE, NORTH CAROLINA

CONTENTS

MYTHS OF MADNESS

CHAPTER 1

YOUR PROBLEM AND MINE

INTO THE physician's office walk a young man and woman, ostensibly for their premarital blood tests, but obviously with more on their minds than a simple procedure that will prepare them for a joyful occasion. With a little questioning, the doctor all too often finds that they are seriously concerned: *Her* mother spent part of one year in a mental hospital, and *his* grandfather died in an insane asylum. Should they get married at all? They want children, but won't they be "sick in the head?" Isn't that the way inheritance works? What can they do?

It is for them—and for many of their doctors, lawyers, teachers, friends, and acquaintances—that this book has been written. Too many human beings have known mental suffering, and still more have had to stand by, watching and trying helplessly to be useful—all because the information they already had or could find in easily available places was confusing, misleading, insufficient, or, in many instances, downright wrong.

In the United States, we pride ourselves on our scientific achievements, and millions of us watch and learn as the feats of our astronauts appear on television. We worry about the teaching of science in our schools, and urge more mathematics and physics for the primary grades. But for many reasons, several of which will need discussion in later chapters, we are, most of us, woefully lacking in scientific information on human behavior. Besides, much of what continues to circulate should have passed out with the horse and buggy.

In the field of "insanity" or "mental illness" we are in special difficulty because a large percentage of the public and, unfortunately, all too many of the professionals whose work forces them to deal with this particular problem still consider it true that "people are just born crazy." Yes, it is sometimes said in more sophisticated ways, and sometimes lip service is paid to the new ideas and theories that have come to public attention; but all too often, the old, outmoded theories influence what is really thought and done.

This is an optimistic book. Very, very few people are "born crazy." The young couple can almost certainly have children without fear. The public can and should know the newest, most important results of the work that is going on in what are academically known as the behavioral sciences. "Mental health" should be more than a phrase in an occasional fund-raising letter discovered among the bills on the breakfast table. And so should its companion phrase, "mental disorder."

You will notice that throughout this book mental and emotional disturbances are not referred to as "illnesses" but as "disorders." This change results from the new awareness among psychiatrists and other behavioral scientists that their patients are not sick in the usual medical meaning of the word. Furthermore, fewer and fewer effective treatments are physical in the sense of involving electroshock, insulin coma, and the like. We still call the institutions for these patients "hospitals," but again, as we shall see, the resemblances to conventional medical hospitals grow fewer with time. Mental disorders cannot be diagnosed by such anatomical or chemical means as urinanalysis or blood pressure or X rays.

The existing standards for measuring mental health and

disturbance are in many ways social and ethical: How far does this patient's thinking and behavior differ from what we call ordinary? Perhaps not very far, and then the question of degree becomes important both for diagnosis and for treatment. But whose standards of behavior and thinking are to be used? There are no machines to count or weigh or measure them.

Another characteristic of mental disturbance also sets it apart: the extreme frequency of its occurrence. Look, for example, at these staggering figures on a representative sample of the population of midtown Manhattan:

2.7 percent of them were incapacitated by mental disorder;
7.5 percent had severe emotional symptoms;
13.2 percent had marked emotional symptoms;
21.8 percent had moderate emotional symptoms;
36.3 percent had mild emotional symptoms.

Only 18.5 percent were judged mentally healthy! Can you think of a physical disorder that afflicts over four-fifths of the citizens of New York? In such a case, we would be inclined to feel that the 80 percent majority were healthy and that the 20 percent were the deviant, sick group. In the mental disorders, we really do seem to have a human problem distinctively different from the physical problems of bodily illness, and to speak of "mental illness" can only confuse the issue and perpetuate outmoded or doubtful ideas and theories.

The older terminology is certainly understandable in historical perspective. The fathers of modern psychiatry were, in the main, medical men, accustomed to dealing with specific and long-identifiable diseases. For many years, neurologists predominated among those treating the mental patient, and Freud himself was a doctor of medicine, whose early thinking clearly reveals his biologically centered training and practice.

This situation led not only to using medical terms but to

classifying mental disorders like physical diseases, and the problems created by this understandable but mistaken technique still plague the profession. The layman may find it hard to believe, but terms that are used every day may mean one thing to one doctor and something somewhat different in a hospital two hundred miles away.

"Schizophrenia," for example, is generally agreed to be characterized by withdrawal from social and emotional contacts, by hallucinations and delusions, by a flatness of emotional responsiveness (or, technically, affect), and by catatonic conditions that may show either stupor and marked muscular rigidity or severe agitation accompanied by stereotyped behavior. But as we shall see, especially in Chapter 6, these symptoms seem to vary from place to place. Is this because of the physicians making the diagnoses? Or is "schizophrenia" used to describe more than one disorder? The difficulties of research on a subject that is by definition so amorphous must be obvious. How does one trace a history of schizophrenia back through generations of a family when each diagnosis may have been different?

The picture of manic-depressive psychosis is even more confused. Here the patients' emotions fluctuate exaggeratedly, from a state of elated agitation to a condition of total despair. But for some reason, there has been a sudden drop in the number of patients admitted to hospitals with this diagnosis. In New York, in 1928, there were 10 first hospital admissions of manic-depressive patients for every 100,000 inhabitants; in 1947, there were 3.7 per 100,000. In 1928, this psychosis accounted for 13.5 percent of all admissions; but in 1947, the percentage was only 3.8. Georgia during the 1950's was the only state in the union with more patients consistently diagnosed as manic-depressive than as schizophrenic. On the West Coast, psychiatrists complain that their students never get to see a manic-depressive during training. What has happened to this particular psychosis since the late nineteenth century when it occupied nearly as much of the stage as did schizophrenia? Perhaps there has actually been a lessening of the disorder. Or perhaps the healthy population is now better able to tolerate mild cases, and so they never reach the hospital to be counted in the statistics. Or perhaps new treatment methods, administered early, keep the patient out of the institution. But more probably, diagnostic trends have changed, and what a psychiatrist would have called manic-depressive fifty years ago, he now calls schizophrenic—depending, of course, on what state he lives in.

"Involutional melancholia" is another category whose boundaries are even more nebulous than those of other diagnostic groupings. In fact, one research team, after much careful work, was unable to find any consistent, traditional picture at all. Yet the term is still used in diagnosis.

Why, you may well ask, don't the people in the psychiatric field get together and straighten out this confusion if it makes so much trouble? Again, history provides the answer, for the neurologists, the psychoanalytic therapists, the biochemical faction—all the heirs of the old tradition, but each pursuing his particular interest within it—have never been able to get together on much of anything. Even within these groups there are splinter groups advocating some theory slightly different from that of their neighbors. These divergences make any sort of joint action virtually impossible (as will become apparent in later chapters), and as a result, they contribute to the public's problem of getting information about the current situation. Not only is there no possibility of a unified center for disseminating reports, but if those reports were made, their disputes and disagreements would make it hard, to say the least, to know what to believe.

This book is intended to simplify a part of that confusion and hardship. We will look at mental disorders in relation to genetics and biochemistry, trying to sort out the useful and valid elements from the old theories of inherited "bad blood" and family tendencies to "insanity." We will also see what is being done in the newer fields of the behavioral sciences, whose findings are either too little known or buried under the debris of superstition, misinformation, and outdated scientific theories. New suggestions about the impact of culture, environment, and, in particular, the family should shed light on what has become an unnecessarily obscure and darkened region.

Because the most satisfactory materials lie in the reports of the people actually working in the various sciences, perhaps a word of caution now can prevent misunderstandings later. No matter how objective and impartial an investigator may try to be, the possibility of error can creep into his experiments or observations from several directions. There may be bias, prejudice in favor of his own theories, of which he is not aware, but which inevitably affects his results. Or there may be uncontrolled factors of which he is not aware, but which greatly alter the outcome. Or there may be a problem connected with his particular material or experimental subjects that makes generalized conclusions of dubious value. Or his statistics, perfectly adequate in mathematical terms, may be misleading in terms of the actual situation.

The Manhattan figures, for example, suggest that emotional disturbance is far more common than earlier writers had known; what now of their calculations? Schizophrenics have usually been studied in hospitals, where it was deduced that they made up about 1 percent of the general population; recent surveys in and out of hospitals find between 2 and 3 percent to be more nearly accurate; what biases have been introduced by restricting research to the hospitalized groups?

An illustration of what can happen, in spite of the best intentions and in a less confused field than psychiatry, began at Mount Sinai Hospital in New York around 1908. It concerned a clearly distinguishable disease of the blood vessels, *thromboangiitis obliterans*, or Buerger's disease (from the doctor's name). Of a first sample of 100 patients, all were Jewish; 76 were immigrants from Poland, and only 2 were American-born. Of 500 in a second sample, only 4 were not Jewish.

Naturally, Buerger concluded that it was a disease primarily of Jews, Eastern European Jews in particular, and he implied that it must be inherited because it was restricted to a single group. From time to time, other physicians reported cases among non-Jewish groups, but not until 1950 did several medical textbooks catch up with the news that while the disease did seem to be more common in men than women, it was connected with no race or country and clearly was not inherited. Buerger had just happened to be working in an area where many Jewish immigrants from Eastern Europe were living.

Or, to see how difficult it is for the public to evaluate biological research in psychology, even though some of the presentations seem impressive, consider an attempt to identify schizophrenics by fingerprints. In the spring of 1962, an article from an AMA journal entitled "Finger Prints in Schizophrenia" was briefly summarized in one of the medical "throwaways" and very quickly reached the newspapers. In its professional form, it must have reached several hundred thousand doctors who are influencing the public's concepts about schizophrenia, even though they may not be well informed on the topic, and, in the newspapers, millions of readers even less knowledgeable. This study of 100 male schizophrenics reported significant differences between them and a contrast group that pointed up the constitutional (that is, physical) and therefore hereditary aspects of schizophrenia.

Let us, however, take a look at the actual study. A series of

100 male patients in a state hospital were thoroughly screened so that there was complete agreement on the diagnosis of schizophrenia. Only males were chosen because of fixed difference in fingerprints, and certain other categories were excluded. The fingerprints of this group of schizophrenics were compared with the Scotland Yard classification, which is based on the prints of 5,000 individuals. The patients had 6.7 percent more whorls than the Scotland Yard series, and almost twice the number of arches, although only 9 percent of the schizophrenics had arches—and 4.8 percent of the ordinary individuals had them too.

Even though the low percentages mean that only a few of these 100 schizophrenic patients showed real differences, these figures seem interesting. But certain other aspects of the study require scrutiny. Classification was difficult and time-consuming and, according to police department experts, not entirely comparable to routine practice because it required the "close application of the rules of classification." Furthermore, some of the fingerprints were difficult to classify at all because of their worn-down appearance, indicating skin dryness in the schizophrenic patients.

It is important to remember here that the diagnosis of schizophrenia tends to some extent to be a local affair. Those 100 patients, so carefully selected in this particular state hospital, might not be representative of 100 carefully selected schizophrenics elsewhere. In addition, the patients were carefully chosen, whereas the same standards were not applied to their contrast group, the Scotland Yard group. Further, this was not a "blind study"; that is, 200 sets of unidentified fingerprints were not submitted to experts for classification into schizophrenic and nonschizophrenic. The diagnosis was known before the fingerprints were examined, and the natural tendency of investigators is to become involved in their own research. But none of these points appeared in news stories.

How is the public to know the full facts? Once again, the suggestion of inherited mental disorder was put before them—in rather spectacular form, but inadequately and misleadingly.

The material in the following chapters will, hopefully, dispel at least some of these misconceptions. A hereditary view, especially in this field, can lead to unwarranted pessimism and unnecessary fear. In other areas of human life, we have been more willing to debate the possible influences of nature as compared to those of nurture; now we must do the same for mental health.

I am arguing here that the case for the inheritance of mental disorder has been overstated, misstated, and badly applied, and this theory has worked to the detriment of the mental patient in his relations with the law, medicine, and even the public at large. But I cannot, nor do I wish to, prove that heredity has absolutely no connection with mental disorder.

We are all born different, and it stands to reason that some of these differences must make us more or less adaptable to the demands of the particular family and the culture in which we live. "Cause" and "connection" are not by any means necessarily identical, however, and if I can demonstrate that there is a view of mental disorder and our inherited potentialities that is better suited to the facts as we know them—but all too often ignored or unrecognized by professional and layman—then this book will have been worthwhile.

CHAPTER 2

THE SUBNORMAL BRAIN AND THE SUPRANORMAL BRAIN

TO THE READER of the daily newspaper, the difficulties of diagnosing mental conditions may seem exaggerated. He regularly sees a stream of appeals for funds to wipe out this or that disorder, usually specifically and unpronounceably named, until, no doubt, the general appeal to "Support Mental Health" seems inexplicably vague by comparison. This is not a book about the more readily recognized and easily defined conditions of the brain, but because of the understandable confusion that does arise, a few pages devoted to them may be useful, if only for purposes of elimination.

Actually, many of these nonpsychological disorders occur only rarely, although the tragedy is no less for the families involved. As a result, it is not uncommon to find combinations of these brain conditions and the emotional and psychological problems that are our chief topic. But for the time being, let us separate the categories.

Most familiar outside the medical textbooks are the cases of mental deficiency, a catchall term that actually says very little about particular causes or cures, but does indicate behavior unacceptable to the world as it is unless special facilities and adequate training are provided—hence the need for financial appeals.

In the most general sense, researchers have found that lower IQ's, mental deficiency, and congenital defect are associated with such a range of items as to preclude any single and simple explanation. For example: lower-than-average weight at birth; prematurity; inadequate prenatal care or none; substandard nutrition during pregnancy; a family that comes from a socioeconomic group lower than the average; a mother who has already had four or more pregnancies; a mother who is either older than the usual or younger; a toxic element introduced prenatally; a readily identified factor in the genes. These are only scattered examples.

One of the most familiar of the causes of brain damage is so-called erythroblastosis. The discovery of the Rh factor in the blood of human beings, following its discovery in the rhesus monkey (hence the name Rh), provided knowledge that a certain percentage of babies are caught in a genetic bind: their own blood produces antibodies in their mothers' blood, and these antibodies do the damage. Some 15 percent of the English-speaking population are Rh negative, and of these 2 or 3 percent are married to Rh negative partners, so that no harm is done. The other 12 to 14 percent, however, face the problem of incompatibility. Actually, contrary to earlier impressions, there is more than one type of Rh difficulty, and the percentage of the various Rh factors in the population varies widely, just as blood types do. Good evidence suggests that not more than 3 or 4 percent of Rh negative women produce antibodies injurious to their offspring. The probability that a child of any given pregnancy will suffer from hemolytic disease attributable to Rh incompatibility when the mother has not previously given birth to an infant with this condition seems to increase through the fifth pregnancy. If the antibodies have not been produced by this time, the likelihood that they ever will is less, and thus the incidence of hemolytic diseases is somewhat lower in the sixth and subsequent pregnancies. The use of so-called "exchange transfusions," when the infant's blood is completely replaced, has lessened the dangers of permanent damage to an Rh baby, and the possibility that scientists will develop anti-antibodies that will protect the child from the outset seems promising.

A much less common but much publicized mental defect is phenylketonuria. About 1 percent of the population carries a gene that when, and only when, it is matched with a similar gene from the other parent causes an error of body chemistry that produces severe mental retardation, usually imbecility. A child so afflicted can often be recognized at birth because of light eye color and hair color that distinguish him from the rest of his family. But so seldom do the carriers of this particular gene marry each other that the occurrence of phenylketonuria is perhaps 1 in 30,000 to 40,000 births, and only about 1 percent of institutionalized defectives suffer from this disorder. Happily, with early recognition, the disease can now be controlled by the elimination of the amino acids that are not metabolized by the afflicted individual, and thus the chances of preventing serious damage to the child are very good.

The recent discovery of the cause of phenylketonuria is a happy chapter in the relation between genetics and medicine, and brings to mind the discovery many years ago that one important form of mental deficiency was produced by an inadequate supply of thyroid hormone. This form of deficiency, hypothyroidism, produced "cretins," children who were mentally and physically retarded. Because endemic hypothyroidism is now rare (adequate and easily obtained iodine in the diet protects against it), and because it is unusual to encounter a newborn cretin, medical schools are often hard pressed to find a case to demonstrate before students. Not surprisingly, the discovery of the relationship between the thyroid hormone and this form of physical and mental defect led to rash statements about the relationship between the thyroid gland and mental disorder in general—a relationship that has subsequently been disproved.

Huntington's chorea produces another form of mental deficiency, extremely rare, but worth mentioning because it fits so well the public's view of inherited insanity. Infants are not affected, for this disorder usually strikes between the ages of thirty and fifty. But it is caused by a single gene (unlike the necessary two for phenylketonuria), present at birth, as are all our genes. In the United States, those afflicted are apparently descendants of two brothers who immigrated from Bures, Suffolk, to New England in 1630. Huntington himself was a physician who described the disease in 1872 after it had occurred in his father and grandfather. The exact number of current cases is not known, but it is estimated to be less than 2 per 1,000 state-hospital admissions. Many of the victims of this dreaded disorder have committed suicide, thus adding to its dramatic impact on the public. But everyone should be informed that all forms of atrophy of the brain are extremely rare and that only a few have been proved to be of hereditary origin. Unfortunately, the entertainment world has dramatized the Huntingtons' curse more than once, leaving some of the public with the impression of frequent occurrence of a form of "insanity." True, most individuals with this disorder end up in state mental hospitals, but as a result of family convenience and governmental policy, not because they resemble schizophrenics. Many a harmless, pitiful, aged person is living in a state hospital too—only for someone's convenience.

An area that is constantly narrowing with the increased practice of preventive medicine is the mental deficiency that is caused by toxic elements passed by mother to unborn child. Responsible for such damage are organisms ranging from the syphilis spirochete to viruses (the best known being the one involved in German measles). But syphilis, for example, is not inherited and can be cured before the harmful substances are transmitted to the child.

Of course, such cure implies prenatal care, and the statistics indicating the lack of such care may come as a shock. In California, for example, county hospitals see only 21 percent of pregnant women during the first three months as compared with private hospitals, who see 70 percent. The first visit occurs in the third month of pregnancy for 25 percent of the patients in county cases and 7½ percent in private hospitals. The State Department of Public Health recently reported that between 10 and 40 percent of mothers delivered in county hospitals have received no prenatal care whatsoever. Coupled with an infant death rate 60 percent higher than that of private hospitals and a maternal death rate 200 percent higher is a 50 percent rate of premature births in county hospitals.

A number of authorities are convinced that there are relationships between prematurity and the incidence of congenital and mental defects and behavior disorders. In California, the incidence of prematurity is more than 7 percent of live births, that is, between 20,000 and 25,000 a year. No wonder these experts feel that the prevention of prematurity would make a much more significant dent in the amount of mental defect than exploration of some of the more esoteric causes of this difficulty.

The highest incidence of prematurity is related to maternal age and to the number of children the woman has borne, additional factors over and above the question of prenatal care. To a certain extent, very young mothers run a significantly higher risk of producing mentally defective children. So do older mothers. To cite one instance: the chances of Mongoloidism increase from 1 in 10,000 in the maternal age group from twenty to twenty-five years to 1 in 2,000 in the age group from forty to forty-five years. Having more than four pregnancies carries an increased risk of mental deficiency in later children. The most striking figures occur in samples of young mothers with closely spaced, large families. Statistics are easier to come by than the reasons for them, but still they can point up some of the differences between psychological disorder and the damaged brains that we are here discussing.

A number of these nonpsychological factors are combined in the unfortunate situation that exists among our Negro population, where studies have shown a special childbirth problem. They may account for a rather high incidence of mental defect (and perhaps, to some extent, for the lower IQ's in a certain portion of this population): the early age at marriage; multiple pregnancies with a resulting increase in prematurity; diet; and the poor quantity and quality of medical care as compared to the ordinary white population. A tendency among Negroes to migrate often, combined with a different concept of the value of preventive medical care, limits their association with the medical profession. Thus the same factors that affect the white population occur in the Negro population in heavier concentration, mainly as the result of socioeconomic conditions.

Our interest in such information lies in the fact that it introduces multiple elements—others in addition to constitution or genetic inheritance—into the theories of causation of mental deficiency. In fact, it becomes difficult, if not impossible, to measure any sort of genetic factor in the overwhelming welter of statistics presented by adequate studies of some of the lower-class families. Witness a report on 200 families receiving aid to needy children. Over 60 percent of the families had four or more problems affecting their economic or social well-being. Fifty-three percent of the families have physical health problems, and 22 percent mental health problems. Twenty-two percent also had problems with physical disability, and 13 percent with mental deficiency. Poor family relationships, demonstrated by homes broken by divorce, separation, and desertion, occurred in 52 percent of the cases. Severe problems of parent-child relationships or extreme friction between parents were noted in 32 percent of these families. At least one member of 26 percent of the families was a delinquent, and in 31 percent a criminal. Alcoholism was a serious problem in over 30 percent. In addition, there were common-law relationships and illegitimacy in 35 percent of the cases.

It would be easy to take the line that these families were in poor socioeconomic circumstances and in poor health because they began with a subnormal genetic inheritance. But, as we shall see in Chapter 7, possible evidence that might suggest such a downward drift (that is, the tendency for the lower classes to be made up of individuals who have moved down because of genetic mutations) has not been substantiated. Yet the close link between the subnormality of the individual and his socioeconomic and geographical position remains. Thus the children of Negroes from Mississippi who now live in Baltimore are in better physical health and have higher IQ's than their counterparts in Mississippi.

But to leave, for the time being, these environmental factors that are already complicating the supposedly clear-cut area of mental deficiency, what of the so-called dull-normal child who has no history of a special gene or a recognized infection or birth damage? Does he stem from stupid parents, have bad teachers, or perhaps suffer from a vitamin shortage as some TV programs would urge us to believe?

Many studies have been done in this field, but no one has been able to add a percentage of heredity and a percentage of environment and come up with an answer of 100. Twenty years ago, there was considerably more confidence that the division could be made, but even then, the typical conclusion tended to be cautious. For example, the combined results of two studies, one done at Stanford in 1928 and one at the University of Minnesota in 1935, came up with an estimated three-quarters for nature to one-quarter for nurture.

In recent years, the tendency has been to put more emphasis on environmental factors, and one outstanding investigator (who usually leans heavily in the direction of biological explanations, believing, for example, that schizophrenia may be inherited) suggests that without evidence of brain damage, human beings at conception are very much alike intellectually, and behave differently thereafter as the result of life experience and sociological environment.

Not every investigator would so neglect the biological, however. For example, the situation of children in foster homes indicates that the correlation between the true parents' intelligence and the child's intelligence remains higher than the correlation between the foster parents' intelligence and the child's, even though the child moves into the adoptive home during the first few months of his life. It is also true that intelligence develops within the favorable environment of the foster home to a level above what would be expected from the true mother's intelligence and, on the average, to a level corresponding to that of children born into homes having the same general characteristics.

Certain educators question the value of such comparisons, however, because they feel that the use of IQ tests as labels has done more harm than good. If a child is labeled "average," it is difficult for him to be anything else because he will be treated as average. Partly as a result of such opinions, some promising attempts have been made to infect ordinary children with the bug of information and curiosity. One Southern California educator, for example, succeeded in raising the average IQ of his college freshmen by 20 to 30 points. But for the time being, we will have to admit the influence of the genes, even as we learn more about the environmental factors, both prenatal and postnatal.

And these factors are myriad. Even the family kitchen has been shown to make a difference in the mental functioning of offspring. Six hundred and twelve women in Norfolk, Virginia, were used in an experiment involving diet. Their children were tested when they were three and four years old, and, on the average, the intelligence of those whose mothers had received vitamin supplements during the latter part of pregnancy was significantly higher than those whose mothers had received inert control tablets. The benefits were most apparent in the group receiving a multivitamin preparation rather than just thiamin (B_1) or just ascorbic acid (C). On the other hand, a comparable study done among Kentucky-mountain women showed no appreciable variation, but it was found that their usual unsupplemented diet was much more adequate than that of the Norfolk group.

In England, a completely different aspect of home life—family discipline—was related to the IQ tests of eight-year-old schoolchildren. Each home was assigned to one of four arbitrarily defined types: demanding, overanxious, unconcerned, and normal. Verbal abilities in children in the demanding group were well developed, both in comparison with the verbal abilities of children from the normal group and with their own practical abilities. Children from overanxious homes had poor scores on the performance tests, on which their average IQ was significantly lower than the average IQ in the normal group. The children of unconcerned parents did poorly on all three intelligence tests, and their verbal abilities were on the whole less well developed than their practical abilities. Twelve of these 118 children had IQ's of 140 and above, and 9 of the 12 came from demanding homes. This is not to suggest that the way to raise your child's IQ is to make your discipline more demanding, although there may be a relationship between the two. That the Russians believe in it, however, should not make us assume automatically that there is nothing in the theory.

Our competition with the Russians has, in fact, notably increased our interest in the gifted child, and certainly there is no arguing the desperate need for creative people in today's world. But actually there seems to be no direct relationship between creativity and a high intelligence quotient as measured by the usual tests. Creativity may be found among the low scorers as well as the high, and a "genius" may be quite as lacking in this important quality as his academically untalented neighbor.

Among interesting new findings in this area are those resulting from a study of children in the gifted - IQ range and a comparison of the families of those who showed creativity in their ability to use ideas, material, and so on, with those who, despite their high IQ's, could not be called truly creative. Statistically, certain family characteristics were found to be associated with creative performance in the children—a family that encouraged expression without domination, accepted regression, and had parents who showed a lack of dependency on each other or on the family as a means of reinforcing the parent's own status. Actually, among those children who rated high in creativity, no family deviated markedly from this pattern. In addition, the characteristic pattern showed parents who had rather well-defined personalities and who were able to express emotions and emotional material, both toward each other and toward the child. Parents did not necessarily have a happy marriage; yet they were rather sure of themselves as individuals, and tended to express feelings toward each other quite directly. They did not demand constant maturity of behavior in the child in order to build up their own images of themselves as parents. Furthermore, the parent of the same sex tended to be more important to the expressiveness of the creative child than the parent of the opposite sex. The authors of the study point out that many of the creative children and their parents must be considered more "emotionally disturbed" than some of the less creative children and their parents—a finding that is important to the eugenic ideas that will be considered in Chapter 11.

While we are speaking of the gifted, and especially the creatively gifted, child, it may be well to consider a favorite myth—the supposed relationship between genius and insanity. Since the public has rather uncritically accepted genius as inherited, it has been only a short step to the mad scientist and the wild-eyed artist as the product of heredity, and thence another short and not altogether safe step to madness at any level of intelligence as inherited.

Sir Russell Brain, the great English neurologist, speculates that although the genius does not necessarily have more nerve cells than the rest of us, the organization of those he has may be different, more complex, and productive of "associative processes of exceptional richness." This possibility does not run counter to the old idea of neuronal patterning—although, as Sir Russell hastens to point out, the old idea has never been explicitly proved. But if we accept the theory of unusual patterns, he feels that the genius may easily veer into mental abnormality, instability, or even insanity. "The form of insanity most closely related to genius is manic-depressive states." On the surface, this is an attractive theory. William Cowper, James Boswell, George Fox, Julius Robert Mayer, and Isaac Newton provide examples of association between genius and episodic bouts of elation and depression.

But the story may be much more complex. For example, the structure of the family in which a manic-depressive psychosis occurs is different from that of the average family. For one thing, the special child (that is, the one selected for a variety of reasons to represent the family's hopes, and so, oftentimes, the family's disturbances) is the victim of much pushing. The family wants to move upward on the social scale and considers success all-important. Thus, many neuronal patterns would seem to be involved—and again there is still no proof for the existence of any.

More simply, it is not difficult to imagine a genius, unable to produce all the time, experiencing despair when he is between ideas. One must spend a good deal of time alone to be creative, and one must be rather autocratic or narcissistic in that one's own ideas and beliefs must come first. The eccentricities that success fosters and that become a kind of personal trademark for the individual can be joined with variations in mood, isolation, and the like, and easily labeled a mental disturbance.

Certainly the whole problem of genius has been given a rather rude shock by the work of Lewis Terman and his associates. Following into their adult lives students who had rated at genius level on their IQ tests, Terman found, contrary to expectations, that they are well above average as well-adjusted individuals. So the association between genius and mental disorder that is so prevalent in the public mind may be a highly selective affair. We tend to remember characters, and we tend to expect the genius to be a character. The genius who is simply doing good work and living a quiet and relatively happy life does not make newspaper copy.

In general, the earlier hidebound attraction of a theory that the capacity of the human brain is largely determined by heredity led to a lack of sophisticated and imaginative research work, and thus people continued to perpetuate the theory. Then the influence of social forces after 1930—from the totalitarian indoctrination of youth to the comparison of the amount of information crammed into the heads of some European and Russian students and into our own—these and other influences have made us reconsider setting limits to an infant's capabilities because we make generalizations about his background. In all probability, the possibilities for teaching people to learn, to be more creative, and to express more and more effectively have been scratched only on the surface. Certainly the future for the development of such techniques is promising.

And hand in hand with our new knowledge in these fields of research and education goes an old expression: *mens sana in corpore sano*. Since the time of Hippocrates, it has been known that the mind influences the body, and vice versa. As psychiatry has played a more important part in medicine, especially since World War II, many conditions thought to be completely organic or primarily so have been relabeled functional disorders. The term "functional" is used by physicians to refer to conditions that are not irreversibly organic and that are considered largely emotional in cause. The long-recognized interrelations between mind and body have led to a new subspecialty of medicine and psychiatry called "psychosomatic medicine." Although, some years ago, it was hoped that certain conditions might be improved by organic changes (for example, that homosexuality might be improved or cured by injections of male sex hormones), these hopes have not, in general, been fulfilled, and treatment remains in the psychiatrist's offices. On the other hand, the discovery that his deafness, for example, was functional has kept many a child from going through life labeled "mentally deficient." More and more often it seems advisable to look at both mind and body in the search for cure.

Most often, I suspect, the layman thinks of psychosomatic medicine as uncovering the psychological problem hidden by the physical symptom, and so it does. But it is also true that organic conditions can simulate purely emotional disturbances. It is important to note that whatever the organic condition, be it brain tumor or infection, the individual's personality will, by and large, determine his mental reaction to it. During the 1920's, Paul Schilder, an eminent psychiatrist, proved that patients suffering from general paralysis of the insane (syphilis of the brain) developed psychotic symptoms that were appropriate to their personalities as they had been before the disease struck. Earlier it had been believed that the area of the brain that had been damaged would alone determine the patient's behavior or symptomatology; and indeed, some forty years after Schilder, many physicians still ignore the no longer new facts of the situation.

Outside his doctor's office, the layman often meets the popular version of this outmoded belief in TV dramas or in magazine or newspaper articles. Perhaps the most familiar involves the nasty old curmudgeon who has his personality completely changed when the brilliant young neurosurgeon discovers and extirpates a brain tumor, leaving only a heart of gold and a benevolent smile for all.

One case recently reported in the press was no fictionalized story. A World War II hero, in prison for larceny and forgery, was discovered by prison officials to have abnormal brain waves. They felt that scarring of the temporal lobes had occurred, possibly as the result of wartime head injuries, and that so-called psychomotor epilepsy caused his criminal activities. The scars did exist, and after their surgical removal, the patient was pronounced cured. His story was featured in a number of newspapers as well as two national magazines: the veteran had been rescued from a disastrous but temporary condition, and returned to society a whole and healthy man. The sad ending: A year later, the hero was picked up again by the police for a similar crime.

This is not to say that organic disorders do not influence behavior. Any one of us is apt to feel grouchy when he has a cold, for example, but the extent of the influence is not usually great. Given the necessity and the time, we could find the relationship of the grouchiness to our usual personality as well as to our present condition and surroundings. And certainly there is no evidence that the miraculous changes reported in supposed fact and avowed fiction are in any sense realistic.

Many disorders involve a combination of emotional and physical conditions, of course, and sometimes it is difficult, if not impossible, to evaluate the relative strength of one and the other. In a simple situation, a child who is doing poorly in school, but has an average IQ, may be found to be seriously in need of glasses; but when his work does not improve when he wears them, it may turn out that his parents are unaware of his average intelligence, and are pushing him toward becoming a college professor. There is also the problem in such a case that his actual intellectual ability will never be known, because what is measured is the configuration of responses produced by whatever his native endowment after it has been acted upon and modified over the years in the particular situations of his life.

A more complicated example of the problems that can arise is presented by a nineteen-year-old youth brought to a large medical center for psychiatric study. He had been a resident at private schools, and had been tutored for many years, but despite the special help, he had been unable to complete more than grammar-school work, and now he seemed to be failing increasingly often. The patient appeared to be somewhat stuporous, out of contact with his environment, and extremely sloppy and slovenly in manner. He was, from all indications, mentally defective.

This young man had come from a very intellectual family in which professional people abounded. His father was considered brilliant, and his mother had had a career before her marriage. The patient's brothers and sisters were apparently normal. But he, from an early age, had been considered retarded and labeled subnormal because he had never achieved a score over 80 on numerous IQ tests.

Despite the opinion of most of the hospital staff that his condition was organic and perhaps progressive, a young doctor began working with him in intensive psychotherapy. Initially, the two made contact through drawings in which the patient described a rather rich fantasy life full of airplanes, bombs, rockets, and other subject matter that involved either explosions or speed.

To everyone's surprise, the patient gradually began to change. After two years of intensive psychotherapy, he was quite different in physical appearance, neatly dressed, and alert in manner. During his third year of psychotherapy, he began high-school courses and, by the end of another year, completed the requirements for college entrance examinations. At this time his father died; and for financial reasons, his mother interrupted his therapy. When last heard of, he was working as a clerk in his home town, while he still kept his scholastic ambitions. Not surprisingly, considering his long history of difficulties, he was not "well adjusted" socially, but even though he kept to himself, he was in good contact with his fellow workers and caused no problems at home.

Quite different was the case of a forty-six-year-old woman seen for an emergency consultation in the hospital because of the sudden onset of very peculiar behavior. She had become extremely frightened, felt that she and her family were in some kind of danger, and claimed that she heard the Lord speaking to her. She wanted to make expiation for her unspecified sins and did not want to have anything to do with her family, friends, or relatives. Physical examination revealed that she had low blood pressure and somewhat bronzed skin, two symptoms that raised the suspicion of Addison's disease. Chemical examination of her blood revealed that she was deficient in the chemical substances extruded by the adrenal glands, and injections of these substances completely and dramatically reversed her mental condition within twenty-four hours.

Interestingly, however, the onset of her adrenal failure had simply highlighted personality tendencies already present. She was a shy and rather isolated person who stayed at home a good deal, either housekeeping or gardening. Extremely religious, she was critical of people who drank, smoked, or did not go to church regularly. Her fairly dependent relationship with her husband had recently been disrupted to some degree by a change in his business that had made him somewhat preoccupied. Having recovered her physiological balance, the patient herself decided to have several hours of conversation with a psychiatrist, feeling that it was time to do something about her social life, and also wanting to improve her relationship with her children.

These two cases illustrate our closely related points: First, psychological factors can mimic organic ones. The nineteen-year-old's "retardation" turned out to be the opposite of organically progressive, though without psychological help, he might have sunk deeper into apathy and further confirmed his childhood label. Second, organic factors can cause profound psychological changes. There was never any evidence whatsoever that the woman's Addison's disease had an emotional basis, yet her initial symptoms certainly resembled a psychotic state. In actuality, the psychological effect of her physical disorder was merely to point up personality tendencies already there, which she was ready and willing to modify for her own satisfaction.

Furthermore, even in clear-cut cases of brain damage, whether it results from the rare genetic defects, from long-term vitamin deficiencies, from birth injuries, or from any number of other possibilities, some pediatricians and child psychiatrists feel that a significant number of the afflicted can be helped by giving psychological attention to them and to their families. But that is not our concern in this book. Hereafter the "mental disorders" discussed will be of the other kind—those disorders whose cause is as yet a matter of disagreement—and sometimes violent disagreement—but which are roughly, and for the time being at least, categorized as psychological.

CHAPTER 3

THOSE POPULAR GENES

LATE IN THE nineteenth century, with the beginning of systematic research into mental disorder as we recognize it today, the hereditary, or genetic, theory was exceedingly prominent—and understandably so. Society in Europe, where the psychiatric research was being done, was class structured and dependent on heredity (in theory at least). If kings inherited their power and citizens' sons went automatically into the family business, if children inherited blue eyes and fair hair, and if the "innate superiority" of the white race was recognized throughout the world, why not assume that the afflictions of mankind—tuberculosis, poverty, mental illness, and the rest—were similarly transmitted from generation to generation? Theories of social degeneracy, based on notions of "protoplasmic inferiority," were rife, and Cesare Lombroso, physician and criminologist, was expounding his idea that the more a man looked like an ape, the more he thought, felt, and acted like one. His crude formulation did not in itself survive long, but it provided the background for later studies of the correspondence between body type and mental disorder as well as, and more particularly, for the lingering belief that criminality was inherited.

Mankind has long thought that there must be some relationship between outward form and inward nature. The redhead is hot-tempered, for example, and so he may be, for the tantrums that would be punished in a blond he is permitted because of his hair. Thus, over the centuries, there has developed a body of folklore and prediction that includes its own fulfillment. If the fat man is expected to be the jolly life of the party, he may very well act that way, no matter what the misery and tension inside. So the old ideas about insanity carried over into the early scientific investigations of schizophrenia. Already common was the idea that such afflictions were the result of "bad blood," a characteristic as inheritable as "blue blood" or "honest peasant stock." In this setting, early European psychiatric geneticists (concentrated particularly in Germany) began their research, and evolved the theory that with some modifications has supporters and surprising popularity among the medical profession today. (The chief spokesman and investigator in this group is F. J. Kallmann, trained in the German school, but now working in the United States.)

Let it be said at the outset: The geneticist who studies human beings labors under several handicaps. The researcher who works with lower animals or plants is able to mate them at will, to examine the offspring whenever and however he wishes, and to breed generation after generation within months, weeks, or in some cases hours. Obviously, human beings cannot be so treated. They mate as they wish, families are small, and a generation is counted as thirty years. Furthermore, the geneticist who is willing to overcome the difficulties inherent in his experimental stock and to work with family histories and limited numbers of subjects may suddenly come up against one family member who refuses to cooperate, moves away, or dies. Thus the human geneticist is often in an unenviable position, and the genetic investigator of mental disorder peculiarly and particularly so. How much easier to question a normal citizen about the color blindness of his mother's grandparents and siblings than to question a schizophrenic about the mental health of his nearest relatives.

It should also be pointed out that much of the research material and many of the case histories presented in this book deal with schizophrenics. Other disorders cannot in the long run be ignored, but the fact remains that right now most attention concentrates on this one area, whether the specific investigation is concerned with psychology, sociology, chemistry, or genetics.

Understandably, it is the schizophrenics who have received a large share of the time and money spent on research studies of mental disorder. Schizophrenia keeps a fourth of the hospital beds in the country full, strikes most often during the productive years of life (fifteen to forty-four), and continues to produce the horror of mental disturbance that the public manifests when it insists that asylums be located far from town. Schizophrenia, rather than the other mental disorders, is what the ordinary man usually means when he talks about "craziness" and "insanity." The terrifying symptoms and the seeming hopelessness of the problem frighten not only the laymen who come in contact with patients, but also those who only hear or read about them in conversation or in news stories. The thought that schizophrenia may be transmitted from generation to generation is indeed a disquieting one, for how can we hope to prevent inheritance?

"Schizophrenia" is, as we have seen, a difficult term to define precisely or even satisfactorily, and when the complications of genetics are superimposed, the layman may well feel far out of his depth. But it is quite possible to understand the basic theories of the psychiatric geneticists without following them into all the minute ramifications that are necessary for their fellow scientists. As a matter of fact, the nonspecialist is greatly helped by one of the geneticist's solutions to his own problem of working with successive generations of intractable human beings: he uses identical (or, technically, monozygotic) twins as his subjects.

Here are human beings who apparently derive from the division of the single fertilized ovum, and thus have identical genetic structures. (Fraternal, that is, dyzygotic, twins, the products of two ova, will not do, because their genes are like those of any pair of siblings, and one might very well have inherited something that the other did not.)

Actually, the problem of finding the twins for such studies is considerable. Twin birth occurs only once in 85 births and only a third are identical. Despite their relative rarity, twins have been used to provide data about all kinds of things. Smoking, for example, is usually presumed to be a cultural phenomenon, but in 1960 a study in Denmark showed that identical twins' smoking habits were more likely to coincide than were fraternal twins' in terms of smoking or not smoking, the amount of smoking, and the form of smoking (cigars, cigarettes, pipes). On the other hand, age, sex, and place of residence also had their influences, and here fraternal twins were more alike than were members of the general population. Thus it is possible to conclude that more than heredity is responsible for smoking habits.

Not only are twins genetically useful. For physician and layman alike, they have a strong fascination, especially when they are identical. As a result, geneticists citing twin cases in support of their position seem to have produced data with more than double impact, which sometimes grows out of all proportion to actual fact, as we shall see.

If identical twins are relatively rare in the population, how much smaller is the percentage of schizophrenic identical twins! But they do exist, of course. In fact, psychotic twins were reported by Benjamin Rush, signer of the Declaration of Independence, among early doctors interested in the phenomenon; but only in the comparatively recent past have there been systematic, scientific attempts to study them. Today, genetics has much more information about differentiating identical and fraternal twins, and modern statistical techniques have progressed far beyond Dr. Rush's casual reports of scattered examples.

The first study of a large group of schizophrenic twins appeared in the 1930's. Among 25,000 patients were found 350 twins (a shade fewer than would be expected in the general population, though not a statistically damaging discrepancy). In 81 of these 350 cases, at least one twin was diagnosed as schizophrenic, but of the 81, 23 could not be assigned definitely to the identical category and so were dropped, cutting the sample to 58. And in 65 percent of these cases, not just one twin but both had been diagnosed as schizophrenic. In one sense, this is an impressively large percentage, genetically speaking, but several things need to be said about it nonetheless.

First, 58 pairs may not seem to justify the term "large group," and, although we shall meet smaller samples, we may question the size of this one. It certainly points up the problems of locating subjects for such studies.

Second, only two of the pairs eliminated because of doubtful identity were both schizophrenics, and it is very possible that differences within the cast-off 21 would have substantially changed the percentage. Probably we should accept these findings only as a general indication of the situation, for the experimenter himself admitted to being dissatisfied with his sample.

Third, and still more difficult to account for—again the investigator noted the problem—in a number of cases (the number is not given), one twin was schizophrenic and the other affected by some other mental disorder.

Identical twins should not behave this way. A single gene, split in two, so to speak, should produce the same identical disorder. And furthermore, it should do so oftener than 65 percent of the time. If another of their genes gave them matching hair color—or eyes or height or noses—no more frequently, the concept of identical twins would need radical revision or be lost entirely, at least to the nonspecialist. Yet this particular piece of research, despite its internal doubts and questions, is still cited by geneticists in support of the inheritance of schizophrenia.

About a decade after this study, the sample went down, and the percentage went up. Among 10,000 patients in Swedish hospitals were 179 twins. Eighty-five pairs were eliminated from the study as being of unlike sex, 23 because one twin was dead, and 2 for other reasons, reducing the number to members of 21 identical pairs of twins and 48 fraternal ones. Seven of the identical patients were schizophrenic. F. J. Kallmann, using the Swedish data, calculated that in 71.4 percent of these cases both twins had schizophrenia. But examination of the data as we have it shows that four out of the seven patients had twins who had never been hospitalized, and two others whose twins had been psychotic for only a short period (and the statistical value of these episodes was reduced when the Swedish research applied to them the technical term "induced," meaning brought on by environmental conditions). Four plus 2 out of 7 leaves 1 case in which both twins were in about the same condition—hardly striking support for the inheritance of schizophrenia. Actually, 5 pairs of twins in the fraternal group were both schizophrenic and showed much more similarity in the form and the development of their mental disturbances than did the identicals—an interesting fact, but one that proves little or nothing about the genetic theory.

Statistically, the figures resulting from Dr. Kallmann's own research are higher and more supportive of the idea of inheritance. In 1946, for example, he reported that among fraternal twins 14.7 percent were both schizophrenic, whereas among identical twins, the figure rose to 85.8 percent—and thus came closer to the near-perfect agreement expected in identicals. Breaking down this figure, we find that when the identical twins are still together, the figure rises to 91.5 percent; when they are separated, it drops to 77.6 percent. Ought we to consider the possibility that environment makes the difference? Actually, by "separated," Kallmann only means separated within five years before the psychosis; and because the ages of his cases range from fifteen to forty-four, with an average age of thirty-three, the environment, presumably, was the same for many years, certainly during the early, formative ones. Kallmann provides no detailed family-history material, so environmental similarity cannot be assessed with any degree of precision beyond a note to the effect that many of his twins continued to live together far past the age at which most siblings separate.

But other specific and statistical questions can be raised on the basis of Kallmann's data without conjecturing about environment. In one report on nearly 700 pairs of twins, for example, 211 showed no other schizophrenics in their family tree (that is, no other family members had been so diagnosed) and 102 provided data insufficient for making a decision about whether or not they did. Kallmann has nothing to say about how he handled these negative cases—nearly half his sample—although the number and the information are crucial. Obviously, negative cases cannot be averaged with positive cases, or the idea of genealogy loses its meaning. Some time before, however, he had said (not speaking of twins) that anyone whose family history did not include schizophrenics could not be diagnosed as such, but must be considered to have a schizophrenia-like psychosis of "exogenous origin," meaning a mental disorder caused by the environment. Why not say the same of these 313 pairs of twins? Surely everything becomes difficult to understand when the proof that a condition is inherited is the citation of cases among those inherited from, but when this proof does not exist, the condition is said not to exist—unless one is talking about identical twins, whose genes, after all, are distinctive only because there are two sets of them. Such a use of statistics makes these twins appear to be far and away more susceptible to schizophrenia than the ordinary population, which is not true. Although they are useful human subjects for the geneticists, they are not creatures apart.

To further compound the confusion, Kallmann (and other supporters of the genetic theory) believes that schizophrenia is a recessive disorder. In genetics, "recessive" is a term applied to characteristics that may not appear in the parent; he or she only passes on the gene that affects the offspring. The brothers and sisters of a patient are more likely to be affected with a recessive disorder than are his children. But Kallmann found more schizophrenic children (16.4 percent) than schizophrenic siblings (11.5 percent) among his sample of schizophrenic patients.

When both parents carry the recessive gene, the chances that the offspring will inherit it rise sharply, so sharply that his finding that 68 percent of the children who have two schizophrenics parents are also schizophrenics seems very low.

Furthermore, instead of finding 100 percent agreement among the identical twins in his sample, he finds 85 percent, an apparent failure of theory that we have met before, although less extreme in this case.

Statistics like these are often explained by "estimates of variable penetrance." Variable penetrance is a theoretical concept used by geneticists to indicate that some genes find it harder to express themselves than others do because of some kind of cellular difficulty. The distinguished geneticist James Neel calls it "figure juggling," and his equally distinguished

Swedish colleague Jan A. Böök talks about "considerable modifications or suppressions as an effect of other genes and environmental or cultural factors." Thus, not all geneticists are rigidly positive about their findings, although, given the present state of knowledge, others of them seem to call upon this particular theory of penetrance when they are in a tight corner.

But leaving the abstractions of statistics for the more concrete evidence of personal histories, let us look at the two cases that turn up over and over again in discussions of the causes of schizophrenia. That they are of special interest is not to be questioned, but that they prove the genetic hypothesis for all time is at least open to doubt.

Their importance lies in the fact that both involve identical twins who were brought up from infancy in separate homes and who were subsequently diagnosed as schizophrenic. Genes the same; environments different—seemingly an ideal situation for studying the nature-nurture controversy. And because such situations are so difficult to find and although the frequent references to them seem to have exaggerated two into several hundred, only these two cases have been reported in all the psychiatric literature.

In the earlier of the two, Kaete and Lisa were both found to be hospitalized at the Herzberg Hospital in Berlin, both diagnosed as schizophrenic. They were definitely monozygotic, and they were also illegitimate. Their maternal grandfather was apparently normal, but the grandmother was said to be "peculiar" and apparently died at the age of forty-two from acute alcoholism. These grandparents had five children, four boys and one girl. Of the four brothers, one, said to have been a heavy drinker, died of tuberculosis. The other three were still alive, all married but without children, and all regarded as rather eccentric. The twins' mother was said to have "a limited mental endowment" and did not do well in school.

As a domestic servant, she impressed all her employers with her peculiar behavior, and at twenty-six she was committed to the hospital for the first time in an acute catatonic stupor. When she recovered, she drifted about from job to job in a very poor environment.

The twins' father was presumed to be a Belgian ship's cook, but he was not traced, and not even his name is known. Two years after the mother's first commitment, the twins were born. At that time she had two attacks of eclampsia, and impressed all the clinic attendants "with her restlessness and unapproachability." Because she was also "completely obsessed with fantasies and gave utterly inane replies when addressed," a second commitment resulted. After she had recovered to some degree, she went out on leave one day and never returned. She lived for a while on charity and on small contributions from her brothers, but, developing tuberculosis, she deteriorated both mentally and physically, and died at the age of forty-two.

Shortly after birth, each of the twins was adopted by a different maternal uncle. Living in different cities and on very bad terms with each other, the uncles gave the twins only a few chances to see each other in their first decade, although there was more contact later. The twins apparently adopted the mutually hostile relationship of the maternal uncles and made unfriendly remarks about each other. Although they did well at school, their uncles independently reported them to be difficult to teach, stubborn, callous, and indifferent.

Kaete had measles at ten; Lisa did not. Otherwise, they developed similarly; both had their first menstruation at the age of twelve, in the same month, and both were the same size and had the same blue eyes and blond hair—they are described as strikingly pretty.

After they left school, Kaete was employed in a factory, while Lisa became a domestic servant. Kaete was seduced at the age of fifteen and gave birth to a baby (who was raised in an orphanage and has thus far been normal). The delivery was uncomplicated, but a few days later she became excited and disturbed, and eventually lapsed into a catatonic stupor. Committed to a hospital in 1928, her condition became worse except for a brief improvement early in 1930. She was readmitted in June, 1930.

Lisa remained a virgin, and continued in domestic service. About the time of Kaete's brief release, she began to exhibit schizophrenic symptoms. Slowly increasing helplessness and emotional indifference reached such a point that she was hospitalized in June, 1930, the month in which Kaete was readmitted. She did not, however, become quite so disturbed as Kaete.

Kallmann feels that this is a classic case, proving the genetic theory beyond a doubt. Because the twins were exposed to utterly different conditions of life, the environment could have played no part in the psychosis. He emphasizes the separation in space and the different surroundings, and he points out that the girls had so little contact that they were completely alienated, and even singled each other out for verbal attack. We do not, of course, have a great deal of specific psychiatric data to go on, but several questions come to mind.

Were the environments so completely different? Two mutually hostile brothers, living in roughly the same socioeconomic circumstances (although in different towns), themselves described as eccentric, reporting two girls as being difficult and indifferent. Two girls brought up in this aura of hostility and eccentricity, both going to work on the same socioeconomic level, both separated from other family members, and both aware that a twin sister existed. Actually, it might be said that Kaete, although she was hospitalized first, was the stronger, for she was out on the street and had an illegitimate baby, whereas Lisa, as a domestic, remained in the relative security of a home. Yet Kallmann suggests that Kaete's activities triggered off her predisposition to schizophrenia. He presents no theory about the precipitating factor in Lisa's disorder, but one vital point is not mentioned—the relationship of the twins from February to June, 1930. At one point, he says that Kaete, after her brief improvement, started doing badly again in February. At another, he says that Lisa's disturbance started in February. But nowhere does he mention their relationship during these months. Surely, despite his statement, the girls were far from indifferent to each other. Mutual hostility argues involvement, however negative. But given no more than a time reference, it is possible to say only that their simultaneous admission to the hospital in June is indeed striking, though far from rare among individuals bound together in hostile-dependent relationships (including nonblood relationships). It is surprising that an eminent authority would stake so much on a single case.

In many respects, the second case is curiously similar. Again the twins, Edith and Florence, were female and supposedly without contact in early youth. They first met at the age of twenty-four, but, again, they had been aware of each other's existence long before. (At the time of the psychiatric report that we have, they were fifty-two.)

A brother, five years older, had run away from home. The mother died when the twins were nine months old, the father remarried, and Florence was adopted by an unmarried maternal aunt. Edith stayed with her father, who became an alcoholic and who mistreated her: she was struck with a razor when she was eight and still bore the scar at fifty-two. She was then put in a children's home where she remained until she was nineteen. Edith declared that when she was living with her father, Florence made trouble for her by telling her father that Edith said he was a drunkard. This story is difficult to reconcile with the statement that there was no contact between them; perhaps what is meant is direct contact. It is important, in view of their mutual antagonism and jealousy, that they knew of each other's existence, because they could hardly have helped wondering who was getting the better breaks.

Edith went to work as a domestic servant, apparently successfully, for she held one job for eleven years, losing it when she was forty-eight. She was said to be pleasant and capable, but felt that visitors to the home accused her of wrongdoing. Reported to have been a superior worker in a glass factory, she would occasionally ask her supervisor if she was causing any trouble among the other workers by her presence. When she was interviewed, she was found to be suspicious and reserved, but without characteristic schizophrenic symptoms.

Although the psychiatrists state that Florence had a happy time with her aunt, she is reported during her childhood as being nervous, afraid of the dark, backward in school, and subject to numerous fainting attacks. She left school at fourteen to become a domestic, but when she stole from her employer she was put in a convent for two years. At eighteen, she had an attack of "nervous debility" with abdominal pain, vomiting, and nervousness, and stayed with another aunt while recuperating.

At the age of twenty-four, having been left some money, the girls are said to have had their first meeting, apparently a rather stormy one. Edith claimed that Florence said she had paid Edith's fare to London, and that therefore Edith was under obligation to her, and Florence accused Edith of stealing money from her purse. Nevertheless, Florence noticed how much alike they were, and she wanted to live with her twin. When she refused, Florence returned to the aunt with whom she had lived since infancy.

The twins continued to see each other from time to time. Both were very religious, and frequently they went to church together. Later, both became somewhat deaf, and each accused the other of feigning deafness; this deafness may have played a part in their delusions that other people were talking about them. If they did not see each other for a time, each accused the other of spying, visiting her place of work, or following her from across the street—in other words, accused her of maintaining contact.

When the aunt died at the age of eighty-five, in 1944, Florence became very depressed, felt that people were saying she ought to get married, and began to hear a man's voice saying "horrible things." She was hospitalized within the year.

The authors' comment: "These monozygotic twins were brought up along entirely different lines." Florence, they point out, had a stable home and an affectionate maternal aunt. Edith lived with a drunken and violent father of whom she was terrified, was put in an institution from eight to nineteen, and then lived on her own. Both twins have the same genetic endowment of intelligence; yet Florence did poorly at school, Edith well. Florence broke down and was hospitalized; Edith lived alone and did well at her work. Florence was convicted of stealing, and Edith was not.

There are resemblances, of course: They lost their mother and to all intents their father, and their runaway brother died early. They were unmarried and guiltily preoccupied with sex. Both were religious. Their work was the same. They were extremely competitive and suspicious of each other, apparently with good reason. Their paranoid symptoms intensified after their first meeting, and they fed on each other in such a way that both functioned adequately until Florence broke down at the age of fifty-two, immediately following her aunt's death. In this connection, the authors' insistence that Florence's home was a stable, happy one in which she lived continuously is difficult to reconcile with her desire to live with Edith, her employment elsewhere as a domestic, and, after her first illness, her visit to another aunt for convalescence.

Once again the emphasis on different environments must come into question. Florence's is assumed to be much superior to Edith's because, on the surface, she had more advantages. But without information about what the spinster aunt was like and without knowledge of Florence's reaction to being the one chosen to be sent away from home (even though her father was a drunkard), it would seem unwise to make value judgments about "good" and "bad" environments.

Furthermore, the description of Edith's disorder is not that of classical schizophrenia. The psychiatrists knew Florence before Edith appeared at the hospital, and it seems possible that the very rarity of disturbed identical twins may have influenced their terminology. Actually, to another psychiatrist, the description of the interview with Edith suggests not schizophrenia but what English physicians usually refer to as "paraphrenia" (that is, paranoia).

As genetic proof, these two cases (and remember, they are the only two) would be far more convincing if the environments were more dissimilar, and if each twin did not play so prominent a role in their combined delusions. Although twins, because of their closeness, may easily become overinvolved in this particular way, persons who are completely without blood ties or early-environmental relationships develop the condition often enough for it to have its own name: *folie à deux*, a kind of shared psychosis. Inheritance cannot automatically be held responsible, and a much more complicated investigation of causes is called for.

In actual fact, a truly scientific study of identical twins is virtually impossible. If a woman were to have twins without knowing it, and if one of them were given to another woman who looked sufficiently like the other and who had just had a stillbirth without knowing it, and if these two children could be studied without knowing it, and if they developed identically in the two different homes, then we would have less complicated and/or biased data about the influences of heredity. Such an experiment would be the scientific parallel of the double-blind experiments that can be used to evaluate new drugs, as we shall see in Chapter 5.

But even in such a situation, factors would remain uncontrolled. One that has been receiving more and more attention of late years is the prenatal environment, long assumed to be identical for identical twins, but now found to vary in hitherto unsuspected ways. Some researchers, for example, emphasize the fact that within the class identical twins, two subclasses exist—monochorionic and dichorionic. In monochorionic twin pairs, both embryos are enclosed within a single chorionic membrane; in dichorionic twins, each embryo is enclosed within a separate membrane. When there is a single membrane, the twins often compete for the placental blood supply, and by midterm, differences are perceptible. Sometimes at this point the weight difference is greater than in the case of fraternal twins, although at delivery this disparity has been reduced to about the same amount, still remaining greater than in the case of dichorionic identicals. It is also common to find that one of the two has some form of circulatory impairment. Because about two-thirds of identical twins are monochorionic, researchers are now beginning to take into account these prenatal environmental conditions, whatever the problem studied.

Lanny and Kris, for example, were identical and monochorionic, and had a significant weight difference at birth. Unlike the earlier cases that we have examined, however, they were being treated for neurotic, not psychotic, symptoms, having been brought to a clinic because Kris had developed a school phobia. They were six years old, in the first grade, and, at their mother's request, in different classes. This separation had brought on Kris's violent reaction against school.

Hospital records and the analysis of five blood-group factors established their monochorionic monozygotic origin. At birth Kris weighed 4 pounds 15 ounces and thus was technically premature (under 5 pounds), whereas his brother was not. Lanny was delivered first and at once began to bellow and show signs of vigorous action. Kris had to be provoked into activity, went to sleep before Lanny stopped crying, and was of a color that suggested circulatory defect; three months later he had an anemic condition that necessitated a blood transfusion. These patterns of behavior continued: Lanny kicked and screamed on the exercise table, resisted restraint during circumcision, and was generally a very active baby; Kris accepted restraint, went to sleep immediately after feedings, and was generally passive and unresisting. Lanny struggled to roll over, crawl, sit, stand, and walk, while Kris watched and then, after his brother had succeeded, proceeded to do the same with very little effort or extraneous activity. By their first birthday, there was little difference between them in terms of weight, vigor, or the like, but Kris had already become the follower, Lanny the model.

Furthermore, their mother was a hyperactive person, unable to relax easily, and uncomfortable about passivity in others. Her mother had become psychotic after six years of inactivity and slovenliness. Fifteen years old at the time, the twins' mother had subsequently become panicky when she stopped work to rest for a moment, fearing that she too would become psychotically passive unless she went on with the household chores at once. It is not surprising, therefore, that by the time the twins were twenty months old, she had a decided preference for Lanny. As a result, she turned Kris over to his father, who had until then been a virtual stranger to the boys. In her own words, Lanny was the "original," Kris the "stamp." "Kris should have been a girl."

Kris at six spent a good deal of time thinking about aggression and counteraggression. As he put it, be careful about grown-ups or "they will cut your throat." This feeling of distance from adults almost certainly increased his dependence on the twin relationship. Separated from Lanny in school, he at first refused to go at all. When he was forced, he cried and protested until he reached the classroom. There he became hyperactive, talking constantly and answering all the questions put to anyone, whether or not he knew the answers. Lanny seemed to accept the separation without any difficulties. But, because their mother felt that he too had problems, "undercover and not as obvious," both were seen in therapy.

The boys were by then about equal in motor vigor, but the old pattern remained in other forms. Lanny, trying to become the man of the family, was loud in declaring his fearlessness and in mastering his environment directly, that is, by action. But when he could not, problems arose. For example, he refused to admit any worry about a trip to the dentist—until he saw the chair and dissolved in terrified tears. Kris's verbal IQ was higher than Lanny's, and he verbalized solutions and feelings. The watcher had become the thinker, while the doer had remained the doer.

Thus in many ways, these technically identical twins were far from identical. Within the first few weeks of their uterine existence, differences began to develop. Then their initial variations in physical activity and passivity were intensified by their mother's reactions. Thus it was environment, both prenatal and postnatal, not heredity, that was primarily responsible.

Constantly, more and more factors are found to weaken the case for identicalness, complicating the already complicated problems of the genetic investigator. Just in the narrow field of divergent sexual behavior in twins (that is, one is homosexual, the other heterosexual), the scattering of influence is wide and numerous: the parents' prenatal fantasies about the sex of the children to come; the difficulties of childbirth; the twins' names; minor anatomical differences; the position of the father in the family; and many others. To invent an extreme example (for almost never do all factors conveniently turn up in one case): Mr. and Mrs. Robert Black want twin boys. The first-born girl arrives promptly, but the second causes many hours of difficult labor. This first-born is named Roberta for her father. She also has a small but distinctive mole on her left shoulder, which her mother and the rest of the family touch and talk about in their attempts to distinguish between the twins, thus giving Roberta a good deal more attention than her sister gets. Roberta, within a few hours or at most a few days of birth, has the advantage over her twin on several counts. As she grows older, there is a tendency for the family to treat her as the desired boy. Therefore, more and more, she models herself not on her feminine mother but on her father, and she grows up so identified with the masculine role that she never achieves a suitable heterosexual relationship, and finds herself with neurotic problems that her less favored but genetically identical sister does not have. What price genes?

That we are a long way from being able to make any firm decision about the causes of mental disorder on the basis of genetic studies alone should now be clear. Not only are the samples small, the statistics suspect, and the conclusions doubtful. Some geneticists, to modify the old nineteenth-century theory of heredity and behavior, have themselves cited the famous case of Chang and Eng, who were far from similar and far from harmonious. Their food preferences were almost diametrically opposed. Cheerful Eng never drank or felt any effects from irritable Chang's alcoholic bouts. In fact, their quarrels sometimes led to blows and once to court. Yet, seemingly, genes and environment must have coincided, because they were not only identical; they were Siamese twins.

CHAPTER 4

THE GENES ACCUSED

WHAT IS IT that the geneticist expects the genes to do? How are they presumed to operate within the body to produce the various mental disturbances? The possibilities are almost infinite, and many theories have been proposed, some familiar as a result of long circulation, others newer and therefore perhaps more exciting. But how much evidence actually supports them?

As are other scientific fields, the history of human genetics is, of course, full of trials and errors. There would be no point in detailing here all or even many of the promising leads that have come to dead ends; but just a sampling of theories proposed, discarded, or still supported, though on slight evidence, can adequately outline the discouraging story of the search for the genes responsible for mental disorder.

Some indication of the far-reaching nature of this search is suggested by the investigation into the possibilities of the pineal gland. For centuries, it has fascinated biologists. In the human being, it is a tiny, almost nonexistent nub, secretly tucked under the bulging of the cerebral hemispheres. Although biologists have established that the pineal is the "third eye" of certain (mostly defunct) lower forms of life, no evidence of function has been established in man. To know about this little pine-cone-shaped object (whence the name) and not be able to assign it a function is enough to suggest to some biologists that the mystery of the pineal and the mystery of mental disorder are connected. Perhaps some genes produce some pineals whose secretions, or lack of them, cause schizophrenia and/or other disturbances of the mind.

No one knows exactly what the relationship between pineal extract and schizophrenia might be, but in the past ten years there has been an increase of interest. It results largely from the fact that pineal-extract injections have been said to raise the level of one of the blood substances thought to be low in schizophrenic patients, and that one chronic schizophrenic was reported cured after the administration of pineal extract. With great energy and ingenuity, the experimenters who made this report were able to refine this extract so that it could be used by other investigators, but the method is by no means simple or inexpensive. The treatment of four patients for two months required a total of 5,000 bovine (beef) pineal glands, crushed to a fine powder and treated with various chemicals to remove those parts to which the body would develop immunological reaction.

Other investigators have tried to substantiate the original findings. Recently, another group at the same hospital was unable to confirm them, and a careful study done in England likewise reports no reliable changes in chronic schizophrenics after a series of pineal injections. At this time, it seems that we might do well to study the "normal" effect of the pineal before assigning it a role in the complicated problem of the causation of mental disorder. The useful results of thyroid research, mentioned in Chapter 2, may have led to overenthusiasm for the influence of the glands and their processes.

With the old ideas of inherited "bad" blood still remembered and sometimes still believed, it is perhaps natural that new discoveries in the field should have raised what have turned out to be false hopes. For example, the inheritance of type in the A, B, O blood-group system has been established for more than twenty-five years; and, understandably, during that time, attempts have been made to prove the hereditary nature of mental disorder by linking it with blood group. Again schizophrenia has been the focus. But early claims made for such linkage have been refuted by later and more careful studies. In fact, the codiscoverer of the Rh factor and a distinguished serologist, Alexander S. Wiener, believes that mathematics has to take much of the blame for the misinformation and misconceptions that exist in this area. A small figure, perhaps 5 percent, impresses the statistician and finds its way into a report or a textbook, whereas the serologist and the medical researcher, looking at the cases themselves, are far less convinced by the arithmetic than by what has already been discovered by other means—this from a man whose work on Rh problems has proved so beneficial. Other possibilities inherent in the blood fall primarily within the research area of the biochemists and properly belong to Chapter 5. Here, however, it can quite definitely be said that the connection between mental disorder and blood type remains unconfirmed by any practical, reasonable means.

If "bad" blood must be discarded, for the time being at least, there does exist another current hypothesis that seems in some ways reminiscent of the old idea of "poor stock." In its less scientific forms it is undoubtedly more familiar to the public than gland and blood research, although the technical term "mesodermal weakness" may sound strange. The mesoderm is the tissue of most of the inside of the body, and supporters of this theory believe that being born with a weak mesoderm—or, so to speak, poor protoplasm—produces an inherited defect that may result in all sorts of disorders, including criminality, tuberculosis, and schizophrenia. Again, Kallmann is the spokesman, and two more of his twin cases will indicate the general nature of this genetic position.

In the first case, one twin was always ahead of her sister in weight, height, strength, and emotional and social adjustment. She had fewer infections, was graduated from school a year earlier, and got a better job. Married at twenty-nine, she had four children. While doing factory work during the war, she came close to having a psychotic breakdown, but when she returned to her secluded, protected home situation, she settled down again, showing some schizophrenia-like symptoms and some mildly paranoid ideas, but never reaching the condition of true schizophrenia.

Her identical twin, on the other hand, had an illegitimate child at eighteen, entered a convent, and had her first psychotic episode. Recovering without treatment, she worked steadily for ten years; then she broke down again, and again recovered within a few months.

In terms of mesodermal weakness, how can these differences be accounted for? Identical twins should, according to Kallmann's own theory, break down virtually simultaneously and to the same degree. (Environmental differences, which might in this case seem to be of considerable importance, must be ignored in the genetic argument.) Kallmann's answer is simple in the extreme: weight.

When the twins weighed at least 130 pounds, their mesodermal weakness did not produce schizophrenia; when they slipped downward, their level of resistance was reached, and trouble followed. During her war work, the healthier twin had lost 25 pounds. Before each psychotic episode, the more disturbed twin dropped to less than 130 pounds, and her spontaneous recoveries were both accompanied by weight gains that brought her up to the specified level. In order to maintain her mental balance, her healthier sister has now been persuaded not to diet for aesthetic reasons.

Both these women did show symptoms of psychological disorder, however different in degree and intensity. But the second case in this category posed a real problem for the genetic investigator: one identical twin was completely healthy, and the other was extremely disturbed. One sister had always weighed 5 pounds or so less than the other. Before she was twenty, she had developed a severe psychosis, was in and out of the hospital, and finally reached what was apparently a chronic state of deterioration. Meanwhile, the normal twin was carefully watched for symptoms that never appeared. Then, gradually and suprisingly, the psychotic sister improved—"unobtrusively except for a steady gain in weight," says Kallmann. When she outweighed her healthy twin by 22 pounds, she too was found to be without symptoms. Both promised never to lose weight again.

An idea of this sort is extremely appealing. Such a simple explanation of and cure for severe mental disorder would indeed be a boon to mankind. But unfortunately the problem is nowhere near solution, for no other evidence supports these seemingly hopeful and spectacular findings. Kallmann's theory of weight and mesodermal weakness allows him to explain an apparent failure of the genetic hypothesis, but not many doctors would be willing to place so much reliance on a five-pound difference, whatever the disorder. This is not to say that physical characteristics are without psychological influence, as we have already seen and will see again. But without further detailed and controlled study, it seems advisable to continue to assume that in such situations loss of weight is the result rather than the cause of mental disorder. It also seems wise not to rely too heavily on the theory of "mesodermal weakness" until more, and more adequate, evidence is produced.

Among the general public, the influence of the genes is probably recognized most commonly in terms of family resemblance—hair, eyes, noses, chins, height, and so forth—and closely related is the presumed association of personality and inherited body build. Most persons know that tall parents tend to have children taller than the average. But in the nineteenth century the application of such common knowledge was carried to extremes, far beyond the physiological facts. Best known is Lombroso's proposal that because an apelike mind and an apelike body went together in human beings (apes and criminals being similar, so he said), human criminals could be identified by their appearance. This particular theory died a well-deserved early death, but not before it had developed the beginnings of present-day attempts at "somatotyping," that is, associating a set of physical characteristics with a set of psychological characteristics. Scientific support for most of these systems is completely lacking, but they survive, especially among the general public, in watered-down versions. "Crazy people" in particular are supposed to be easily identified. When nice ordinary-looking Mr. Smith down the block beats his baby son to death, we are taken by surprise because he didn't "look" crazy.

High on the list of disorders still associated with inherited bodily characteristics is homosexuality. Many people still cling to the belief that a slight, feminine build is the cause of male homosexuality (and vice versa of female); they feel that in some vague way these human beings are partly male and partly female at birth as a result of their physiological makeup. A natural corollary of this unscientific idea is that behavior can be predicated on physical appearance, and it leads to the sort of unhappy situation that we find in *Tea and Sympathy*.

If there were inherited differences, biochemical analysis would distinguish homosexuals from normals. But all such studies have been negative. As recently as 1961, a London psychiatrist, working with 99 transvestites, almost all of whom were overtly homosexual, found no genetic or endocrine peculiarities. Their problems were clearly psychological and not the results of inherited physiological characteristics.

But despite the negative results of such biochemical studies, the genetic theory of homosexuality continues to be supported by a large number of psychiatrists, especially in Europe. Some years ago, Kallmann reported on 44 pairs of identical twins who were homosexual. He felt that the fact of being a twin could have had no influence on their development because their case histories reported no sex play between them, and that therefore the extraordinary agreement of their symptoms must result from genetically determined factors. But since then, a number of reports on the psychology of twins have appeared, all of them refuting his position. Especially important is a study of four sets of identical twins; it is particularly helpful because the sex cells and general biology of the subjects were examined as intensively as the psychological makeup. The very thorough biological studies showed absolutely no detectable difference in any of the cases. Psychologically, however, twins may sometimes react to being twins in two unfortunate ways. First, each may completely lose his sense of personal identity (technically called "inverted identification"). Or, second, each may develop a sense of personal identity by linking himself to a different parent, as our imaginary Roberta in Chapter 3 associated herself with her father ("everted identification").

This situation was exemplified in the actual case of Tom and Dick. Here again, careful testing showed no biological differences between the twins, yet Dick was leading an active homosexual life while Tom was having a series of affairs with women older than himself.

It was Tom who came for psychiatric help. Dick was willing to provide information, submit to the tests, and have twenty-five hours of free-association interviews when he was paid for his time, but he had no interest in therapy or in changing his sexual orientation.

Their parents had a daughter and wanted a son when the

twins were born. The two boys were immediately distinguishable because Dick had a more pronounced split in his lower lip. For this reason and because he was supposedly the weaker, he was singled out for special attention by his mother. Tom, however, she associated with a difficult labor, which she blamed for many subsequent physical ailments, letting Tom know that they were his fault. Rejected by his mother, he found love and comfort in a young nursemaid and his father's mother. In addition, Tom had been named for his father.

So a small physical difference, not genetically determined in any sense but caused by a defective closure in the median labial fissure, starts a chain reaction, leading one twin to identify with his mother and become homosexual, and the other twin to identify with his father and grow into a more usual relationship with women.

It may be worth pointing out that it was Tom who sought psychiatric help, thus adding himself to the statistics of the mentally disturbed. Dick, whose homosexuality certainly constitutes behavior usually associated with disturbance, would never have come to the attention of the profession because he felt no need of help. Tom would more or less automatically be diagnosed as neurotic, but what about his brother? Once again, the problems of definition and the source of data arise to plague the search for causes of mental disturbance.

Furthermore, the tendency for the old ideas to hang on despite lack of data and negative data—to the detriment of the exploration of new ideas—is illustrated by the treatment of homosexuality in a leading psychiatric textbook. Although a fairly recent study is cited, proving the cells of 50 male homosexuals to be male in all cases, the authors continue to support the older biological hypothesis and emphasize Kallmann's identical twins. They say nothing about his fraternal twins, who in 40 percent of the cases were both homosexual. Because fraternal twins have the gene makeup of ordinary brothers and sisters, the large size of this figure would seem to warrant some examination. Besides, the data were reported for males only. It is well known that male homosexuals are easier to spot than female, for women can live together and express affection physically without exciting comment. A woman who does not marry is a "spinster," but a bachelor over thirty-five or forty may be suspect in terms of his maleness.

The stubbornness of the attitude that sees homosexuality as "constitutional" is encouraged by the belief that it just must be so because "intersexed" members of lower animal species are not infrequent. One such hypothesis—the constitutional homosexual represents an intersex, an individual genetically of one sex but morphologically (that is, in bodily structure) of the other—is an attractive theory, but unfortunately no one has been able to supply the evidence to support it.

On the other hand, and once again, the attitude of the parents can have a great deal to do with the child's sexual identity, whether or not he has a twin. For example, children actually bisexual as infants had surgical and plastic operations to remedy the conditions, and surprisingly the success of the operation depended little on the extent to which the infant had been male or female. What was of great importance was whether the parents wanted a boy or a girl. The outcome was best in those cases in which, regardless of the physiological situation, the surgeon followed the wishes of the parents. No one has yet claimed that such wishes are genetically determined.

The pineal theory, the blood-type theory, the mesodermal theory, the body-build theory constitute a sampling of hypothesis about how the genes work to cause mental disorder. But the theory that sometimes seems to have by far the most supporters is one without a technical name, although it might well be called "the upside-down theory." That is, the action of the genes is simply taken for granted, and because parent and child, brother and sister, behave in similar ways, it is assumed that the behavior is genetically caused. This position naturally influences diagnosis, diagnosis influences the statistics, and we return full circle, having used the hypothesis as proof of the hypothesis. A look at the family studies conducted by geneticists will demonstrate this point.

Typical of books in the field twenty-five years ago is one that puts first in its definition of schizophrenia "particular constitutional types," although the authors go on to point out that the common symptoms of schizophrenia are so general that statistical studies should be regarded skeptically, and that only understanding of individuals seems possible. Cases of schizophrenia were not common in the heredity of their sample, only a small number of parents were psychotic, and, in general, the occurrence of mental disorder was striking only when the category "odd personalities" was added to those more specifically diagnosed. In fact, within the diagnosed cases were included not only psychoses but also feeblemindedness, alcoholism, neuroses, and epilepsy—a range so wide as to be meaningless, even without the entry "cousin not mentally right," considered a paternal "taint" in one case.

Had these authors been able to free themselves of traditional ways of thinking, they might have been impressed by how infrequently the heredity factor appeared in their own data. But as it is, the book remains an argument for genetics despite its own evidence—and apparently just because the genetic theory was there. (One of the authors, however, changed his position later, and became a distinguished social psychiatrist.)

Few of the statistics that emerge from geneticists' family studies are overwhelmingly impressive. The percentage of schizophrenic siblings of schizophrenic patients is about 5, and the percentage of schizophrenic parents ranges from 4 to something under 2. (Kallmann finds 14 percent for siblings, 9.3 percent for parents, but these higher figures may result from the particular statistical technique he used, the abridged Weinberg method.)

One question that naturally comes to mind is how even these figures are arrived at. Again, of those identical twins so often referred to, would Edith have been diagnosed as schizophrenic if the psychiatrists had not known Florence?

So the old problem of diagnosis comes back to plague the findings. In schizophrenia diagnosis cannot be made in an objective and mechanical fashion as it can in diabetes or tuberculosis, and sometimes the theoretical position of the diagnostician interferes with what is at best a tricky proposition. More than a few quite frankly use a history of schizophrenia as a way of diagnosing, perhaps justifiably. But should they then turn about and use the case so diagnosed as "proof" of the genetic theory? One admits to counting twins who have not been diagnosed as schizophrenic because "it would seem captious to exclude them as in every case schizophrenia is more probable than normality or any other diagnosis." It is a long road between the normal and the schizophrenic—and there are psychoses other than schizophrenia. One could wish for more precision.

Furthermore, the human geneticist's difficult sample continues to complicate matters, for how is he to get definitive information about all the relatives of a patient? In one instance, 5,776 people were considered before the final figures were determined, but at the time 1,926 of them were already dead. No doubt authoritative data could sometimes be had, but on occasion unprofessional opinion must have served. "Cousin not mentally right," as used in the older study, sounds very much like the product of hearsay.

When the family member is dead or otherwise unavailable,

much information is obtained from their hospital charts, but often these seemingly accurate and professional sources contain insufficient data, or are positively misleading. Out of 50 schizophrenic women whose charts indicated that they came from an environment without unusual stresses, 8 were found to come from homes in which the family relationships were extremely peculiar—a finding that appeared only when the homes were actually visited.

But assuming the usefulness of some of these genetic studies, we ought to compare them with others equally or more scientifically conducted and producing quite opposite results. For example, a group of Norwegian seamen with a high incidence of schizophrenia had families with an incidence *lower* than average for the population of Norway. Again, among the relatives of 100 schizophrenic children, there was no hereditary trend or unusual increase in the occurrence of the disorder. And in another instance of 381 children, each of whom had one schizophrenic parent, 86 of the children showed emotional or social disturbance; but of 500 children with no psychotic parents, 145 were disturbed. Some of these findings may be the result of chance, given the size of the samples, but they certainly argue against a clear-cut genetic theory.

Nevertheless, the genes continue to be held responsible in some vague, indeterminate way, and diagnosis by heredity continues despite lack of evidence. By its very nature, this process tends to perpetuate the genetic theory. It also leads to some rather farfetched assignments of genetic responsibility, a sample of which is worth examination.

Take, for example, Charles F., a four-year-old referred to a child psychiatrist by a pediatrician because of retarded speech. A community guidance clinic had already diagnosed infantile autism (an extreme and complex psychological disorder), declared him emotionally disturbed and in need of years of treatment, and recommended psychotherapy for his parents too.

There was no mental illness on either side of the family; but language and learning retardation, as well as left-handedness, were not uncommon. The retardations were reported by his parents to be outgrown in time. Charles had an older brother whose motor development had been slow, and who was still clumsy. He had not talked until he was three and a half, and he had been kept in kindergarten an extra year. But at thirteen he was described as doing well in his normal grade in school and being a well-adjusted boy. His older sister, eleven, was left-handed, but not retarded in speech or reading. Although Charles did not talk, had a simple play pattern, and was restless, he fed and toileted himself and helped with his dressing. He had never been anxious or phobic, did not suck his thumb, masturbate, or rock his body. He appeared to be ambidexterous. His parents were said to be neither overanxious nor detached during the interview.

The doctor recommended that nothing be done to disrupt the family circle (presumably meaning no therapy, though why this would be disruptive is not specified), that Charles be encouraged to more mature behavior, and that he be put in a day camp and nursery school soon. She saw no symptoms of infantile autism, diagnosed familial retardation of language, and expected him to talk very soon. Six months later, Charles had not improved but was, according to his mother, "worse"—stubborn, negative, and given to temper tantrums. His mother was disgusted with the few words he did try to say and irritated him into a tantrum by deliberately misunderstanding his wish for a drink of water during a visit to the clinic. He had been accepted in a nursery school, where his mother was certain he would not do well.

The child psychiatrist advised the pediatrician to give Charles a tranquilizer until he could adjust to school and get away from his mother during the day. Her diagnosis was unchanged. Poor Charles is thus tagged with the diagnosis of familial retardation of language, presumably on the basis of the family history provided by his parents, who are certainly not experts. Meanwhile, his behavior disturbances increase, and no help is provided, for historically he will outgrow his troubles. There being no report of mental disturbance in the family, it is inconceivable that he should be diagnosed as a disturbed child.

Elaine C., on the other hand, came from a family with a history of schizophrenia, which her overanxious and overprotective parents tried to minimize. They were reluctant to have the doctor see her alone, because they were constantly correcting or explaining her behavior. The little girl was restless and constantly touched parts of her body. Her speech ranged from baby talk through echolalia, mimicry, and neologisms to intelligent conversation with the doctor and with imaginary objects. On this basis, a diagnosis of childhood schizophrenia seemed justified to the doctor. Within a year or two, however, Elaine would function normally in school. Day camps and kindergarten were suggested to keep her away from home, and a mild tranquilizer was recommended to help her behavior.

Two years later, Elaine's parents had her undergo a series of psychological tests because a relative with an emotionally disturbed child had been referred to a clinical psychologist. This psychologist recommended that Elaine be put in an institution while her parents had psychotherapy, and they came rushing back to the first doctor, wanting to know why she had not done the same. Elaine was by now doing better than average work in first grade, after a year of kindergarten and a summer of camp. Her speech was close to normal, she did not handle her body, and she was excessively restless only toward night. The doctor, without specifying her diagnosis at this time, recommended only a tranquilizer for the evening disturbances. This case is even more baffling than Charles's—at least in terms of what is reported. Was Elaine truly schizophrenic? The evidence is slight. But she did have a family history of schizophrenia. Does it account for the diagnosis? She certainly improved rapidly and without treatment. But why had no treatment been recommended for a schizophrenic child? Because genetically caused disorders cannot be treated?

Two points of similarity stand out in these and other cases. The first is the recommendation of tranquilizers to take care of specific areas of disturbance. In the next chapter, the question of tranquilizers and their relationship to a belief in the organic causation of mental disorders is dealt with as a whole, so here we need only mention the doctor's prescriptions. Second is the suggestion that the children be placed in school or play groups—away from their parents. Does this not imply a psychological trend of thought (which we will discuss in Chapter 8) quite out of keeping with the doctor's genetic position? What difference can it make if the children's difficulties are the results of their genes? One suspects that this doctor is intuitively a good clinician, and responds to the psychological elements in the situation even though they are not in keeping with her theory.

The genetic data, however, seem of doubtful value, as Charles continues speechless, negative, and hostile, and Elaine progresses normally. Each is labeled with the family diagnosis, and the genetic theory is established, but what comes of it? Perhaps the ungenetic suggestion of contacts outside the family circle will help them both. Meanwhile, these two cases demonstrate the extreme of vague adherence to genetic theory. Hearsay family history becomes more important than the child himself, and he then becomes an additional statistic in that history. There is a lesson here: Despite psychiatrists' best intentions to be objective, if they are biased toward genetic causation, they are more pessimistic and fatalistic in approaching the patient. But this is not to say that on the other side of the argument biases don't occur too!

CHAPTER 5

A SALK VACCINE FOR THE MIND?

IN RECENT YEARS, the biochemists have made heavy contributions to the daily newspapers and popular magazines—and for understandable reasons. Wouldn't it be spectacular if someone discovered the pill or the shot that controlled mental disorder as insulin controls diabetes? Any glimmer of hope is greeted with enthusiasm and, unfortunately, exaggeration.

Most vividly reported have been the experiments with chemicals that produce symptoms similar to the symptoms of psychoses—the so-called psychotomimetic drugs. Human guinea pigs of all sorts have subjected themselves, for scientific purposes, to old and new compounds that change behavior. Actually, of course, not all this information is new, because mankind has known for centuries about the hallucinations produced by peyote (that is, mescaline), for example, and the strange dreams of opium, but only recently has there been systematic study of their possible relationship to mental disorder.

As the layman sees it, in the simplest terms, the assumption underlying all this research is that the scientist can learn about the physical states that accompany the "psychotic" behavior —the changes in blood pressure, heart rate, urine, all the things that doctors check—and then develop drugs to counteract them. Presto! a cure for mental illness.

Or the discovery can come from the other direction, so to speak. For example, one such experiment began with the knowledge that the tranquilizer reserpine, apparently beneficial to disturbed patients, reduced the amount of a hormonal substance called "serotonin," which is known to be indispensable to the proper transmission of impulses within the brain. Furthermore, D. Wayne Woolley of the Rockefeller Institute found that large doses of serotonin or serotonin-like compounds caused schizophrenic-like symptoms in normal people, and in 1954, he advanced the theory that schizophrenia was related to an excess of serotonin. The newspapers were generous of their space, and many a layman must have been convinced that the final answer was at hand.

But Woolley was merely advancing a theory, and he continued to work intensively with it and with additional data. In 1961, having developed a new and refined method for detecting serotonin, he reported that he had found none in the spinal fluid of any normal people—and none in the spinal fluid of 21 out of 22 schizophrenics. But in both groups he did find large amounts in the cerebral cortex and announced that differences must now be looked for there. After seven years of work, he suggested a reevaluation of all research and possibly a change of focus. This, however, was not exciting copy except to the medical journalist; the daily newspapers ignored the story, and the layman's latest information is the 1954 report —a far more hopeful one than the situation now warrants.

A somewhat similar story involves ceruloplasmin, a form of serum copper, which was found in larger than usual quantities in the blood of schizophrenics. But two factors counteracted the initial enthusiasm that greeted this discovery: It was known that the same compound occurred in greater quantity during pregnancy and during many diseases. And with each later experiment the amount found in schizophrenics declined. Nevertheless, the so-called Ackerfeldt test was proclaimed to be of the utmost importance for schizophrenia by two national magazines within a two-week period. Needless to say, they published no retractions when the negative evidence came in.

Extremely interested in this theory is a group at Tulane University. Their studies over a period of years have shown the same decline in ceruloplasmin levels that others have, but in 1956 they modified the original position by presuming a qualitatively different form, which they called "taraxein" (from the Greek and meaning "confusion"). This they isolated and tested, and their reports indicated that it produced behavioral and electroencephalographic changes in monkeys. When it was given to prison volunteers rapidly and intravenously, their reactions made the headlines—paranoid ideas, auditory hallucinations, catatonic behavior, disorganization, and so on—schizophrenia produced in the laboratory!

Unfortunately, independent investigations have not been able to duplicate those findings. One group used comparable subjects and controls, but found that only 5 out of 20 cases showed disturbances parallel to those originally reported—and those disturbances occurred just as often in the control subjects who had been given substances other than taraxein.

In another experiment at Tulane, a young doctor (a resident in psychiatry) was one of the subjects, and there is available not only the experimenter's report on his behavior but also the detailed report of his psychoanalyst about his reaction. The subject knew that he was to get either a harmless saline solution or a dose of taraxein that had made a monkey catatonic. The resident experienced an uncomfortable flushing, which could have been caused only by the ammonium sulfate used in the preparation of taraxein. Because this chemical is not used in the control substance (saline), it is difficult to imagine that a young physician would not know which substance he was receiving. At any rate, there followed a period of introspective thought, with now and then mild mental disturbances not at all out of keeping with the anxious situation and his expectations of an extreme psychotic reaction. But the report of the experimenter was longer and more detailed than the patient's. The difficulties of thinking, autism, bodily estrangements, and suspicion that he recounts do not seem to be entirely compatible with or justified by the subject's report.

While the work at Tulane goes on, biochemical researchers elsewhere have been making other discoveries about suspect substances in the blood. Recently hospitalized schozophrenics, hospital staff personnel, and prison inmates failed to give any encouragement to copper research when no differences occurred among the three groups or between the acute schizophrenics and the chronic patients. The quantity of certain enzymes that promote oxidation in the blood showed no change even when stress-inducing drugs like adrenalin were given, and anger and pugnaciousness about taking blood samples did not raise the levels, although either the drugs or the emotions might have been expected to do so. (Furthermore and somewhat incidentally, this experiment weakened another chemical theory involving adrenalin-breakdown products in the blood.)

In particular, the oxidation substances were strongly related to liver damage, not to schizophrenia. And in general, all the differences in blood substances tested seemed to result from the influences of diet or other environmental factors. For example, the diet of state-hospital patients may very well be low in vitamin C, the lack of which affects the oxidation-reduction processes involving copper and thus influences the statistics.

More and more, research workers are discovering how necessary it is to control or at least consider these apparently extraneous and external factors. Seymour Kety and his associates at the National Institute of Mental Health recognized the need for the adequate preparation of schizophrenics for biological testing and the need for a comparable control group. Therefore, with great care, they set up a ward at the clinical center in which a group of young schizophrenic males was matched with a group of conscientious objectors who volunteered for the experiment. Both groups received identical diets, exercise, and so forth. The work is still in process, and the findings will be reported over the next several years.

This interest stemmed in part from the experience of two NIMH doctors who were studying the excretion of phenolic acids in urine. It had been reported by other workers that schizophrenics excreted phenolic substances that were different from those found in normal people, and these were assumed to be the result of some abnormal metabolic process in the schizophrenic. As a result of the alertness of the NIMH investigators, however, it was discovered that chronic schizophrenic patients tend to drink a good deal of coffee, partly perhaps because it is a stimulant, and partly because they have little else to do and having coffee provides social contact. These investigators therefore studied the breakdown products of ingested coffee and, to their surprise, found that the phenolic substances reported by others actually came from the coffee, not the mental disorder.

Some of the most spectacular biochemical experiments have involved mescaline. It has been longest recognized of the hallucenogens and, furthermore, has had an unusually lucid and literate spokesman in Aldous Huxley, who in 1953 agreed to be a guinea pig for one of the tests. His *Doors of Perception* is well worth reading as a detailed account of the expectations, sensations, and reactions of one experimental subject.

But even as one reads, it becomes apparent that Huxley never loses sight of the difference between the normal subject and the true psychotic. If in some cases their behavior seems to be similar, he admits that he has had only some "inkling of what it must feel like to be mad," and when he writes of the better experiences under the influence of the drug, he says "That they *are* better seems to be self-evident to all mescalin takers who come to the drug with a sound liver and an untroubled mind." Perhaps an "untroubled mind" is the key to the dubious quality of many of these experiments, for Huxley never equates his experience with schizophrenia itself as others tend to do.

Recently a more detailed and scientific statement of the distinction between the experimental subject and the schizophrenic proposed that although certain of the artificially induced symptoms do parallel some of the symptoms of the mentally disturbed, the differences far outweigh the similarities. Characteristically, the schizophrenic withdraws from personal contacts, but persons with drug-induced "psychoses" prefer to have someone to talk with. And when they talk, they sound "drunk," but what they say is related to reality. The schizophrenic is vague and highly symbolic in his language, hard to understand. Furthermore, he shows no concern about his inability to communicate, whereas the drug subjects are upset about their difficulties.

Hallucinations are considered symptomatic of schizophrenia, and the patient usually insists that they are real, stubbornly refusing to have them argued away. The experimental subjects are much less resistant, much more open to suggestion. Besides, their hallucinations are visual, the schizophrenic's auditory.

Delusions are common among the hospital patients, but the experimental subjects seldom have them, and when they do, they do not talk about them voluntarily.

Both groups are preoccupied with physical feelings, but in different ways. An experimental subject explains his nausea on the basis of his role in the experiment, while the schizophrenic attributes the agony of a severe ulcer to a devil who is shoving a hot poker into him. Fundamentally, then, the undisturbed maintains far more contact with reality, and mescaline provides no conclusive evidence about true psychotic states.

Despite these negative findings, however, no one would wish to issue a blanket order to all biochemists, forbidding them further research on mental health. In the 1930's, for example, they discovered that certain vitamin deficiencies can affect the nervous system and, in severe form, cause psychotic episodes that are cleared up by restoring the vitamin. Certainly such knowledge is invaluable depite the fact that these psychoses are not schizophrenic or manic-depressive. And there is always the possibility that additional valuable information will be uncovered someday. Even negative findings clear away some confusion. But the suggestion that the biological discovery of cause and cure is just around the corner misleads a helpless public; the solution is not at hand.

What of the tranquilizers? the public asks. They are the concern of the biochemist surely, and their influence is widespread beyond a doubt.

As an illustration of typical expectations, let us look at this report:

> In a group of eighty-five patients treated, fifty percent showed decided improvement and seventy-five percent showed some. Patients who had been wantonly destructive became more placid and clean; those subject to violent outbursts became better adjusted with their environment, and their activities were more easily directed into useful channels following treatment. Patients who required tube feed-

> ing took food voluntarily after two or three days. The most lasting improvement was found in those cases previously regarded as having an unfavorable prognosis [course]. When one considers the changes in the environment of the patients treated—lessened disorder, confusion, and untidiness and conservation of energy for the nurses and other employees, the results are still of greater value. There is marked reduction in the waste of clothing and bedding through tearing and soiling, fewer articles have to be repaired and laundered, and fewer nurses are required to care for the disturbed patients. One nurse explained: "Before these patients were treated, I had to struggle with them every morning to get them bathed and dressed. Fights were frequent occurrences. Now I can supervise the bathing of many of them alone!" Failures occur from the fact that when improvement does not take place in a few days, the drug is stopped when it should be continued.

This is the kind of spectacular improvement that the public has come to associate with tranquilizers. But to be perfectly honest, it was written in 1926—and it was written about bromides. No one today believes that bromides *cure* mental illness; in fact, they are not even used as calming agents in mental hospitals. They, like the tranquilizers, are part of a long story.

Since the beginning of recorded history, there is evidence of man's search for social and chemical means to curb his anxiety, and thus ensure the possibility of greater satisfaction in life. The most nearly adequate substance before the appearance of the tranquilizers was alcohol. Herb concoctions—poppy juice, hashish, bromides, barbituates, and the like—have had sufficient disadvantages to prevent their widespread or completely satisfactory use. These substances either induce intoxication and sleep or so modify sensory and intellectual performance that their effects still leave much to be desired. Another important drawback is that many of them interfere with communication between people, and so introduce other dissatisfactions. But by far the overwhelmingly important argument against their use, of course, is the possibility of addiction.

The tranquilizer introduced a new era to psychiatry because the patient could experience sedation without gross sleepiness and without danger of addiction except in unusual circumstances. Patients may, however, become habituated to tranquilizers (that is, abnormally dependent on their use). In addition, most of these chemicals have unpleasant side effects, and occasionally have caused death by damaging the liver or the bone marrow.

It is well to remember in considering the group of drugs known as the tranquilizers that, from the psychiatrist's point of view, their major purpose is to modify "abnormal" or "offensive" human behavior to fit socially acceptable patterns, and thus increase the possibility of response from the patient's immediate environment, that is, his family, the people caring for him, anyone in contact with him.

Too often, the man on the street thinks of a tranquilizer as doing something to the brain cells that corrects the individual's craziness. This manner of thinking, stemming directly from such medical examples as the action of penicillin on bacteria, does not do justice to one very important factor: the emphasis put on the social acceptability of the individual's behavior. Many a relative of a mentally disturbed patient has said how pleased he was with John's or Jane's improvement when, in fact, that improvement consisted in John's or Jane's being a talking somnambulist. With some patients, this state is clearly preferable to their being a danger to themselves or to others, but it is not the kind of "recovery" that psychiatrists earnestly seek.

The first of the tranquilizer group burst onto the American medical scene after a quick trip across the Atlantic about ten years ago. They owe their origin to the fact that investigators studying the antihistamines in the early 1940's felt that some of them had peculiar calming properties; many patients suffered from drowsiness as a side effect to their use.

The first, and in some ways the most effective, was a derivative of rauwolfia called reserpine. Although rauwolfia plants had been known for hundreds of years since their discovery in India, it was only in the 1940's that the active ingredients were isolated. Today, reserpine has largely disappeared because of its undesirable side effects. But the second-oldest tranquilizer, chlorpromazine (known as largactil in Europe) still remains one of the most potent; its use is primarily restricted to hospitalized patients. Since then, a rush of new compounds has made it necessary to use computers to scramble the alphabet and come up with enough names to go around.

The discovery of the tranquilizers caused an almost immediate and unwarranted upsurge in the number of scientific articles purporting to link their action with the site of origin of various mental disorders. Most of these studies linked themselves to serotonin, with some individuals reporting that the tranquilizers decreased the amount of serotonin, some that they increased it. We have already seen how Woolley, after seven years of investigation, has reevaluated his entire research project.

As the years have gone by, the tranquilizers' potency seems to be subsiding, even as their proper place in medical practice is being found. Most important is their use to reduce the patient's anxiety sufficiently so that he can communicate more effectively with his social environment, including perhaps his psychotherapist, and thus move forward to a better social adjustment, which hopefully can be maintained without the drugs.

One of the chief drawbacks to the use of tranquilizers is not the infrequent side effect, but the temptation for the physician to let the drug be enough. Accustomed to prescribe for immediate relief and the improvement of clear-cut symptoms, he too often lets understanding of the patient's behavior become secondary or nonexistent. As a result, there is no help for the real problem, the symptoms break out again —or in a different guise—and nothing, in effect, has been solved. Early medical reports on tranquilizers praised them unqualifiedly, but more recent papers emphasize the need for psychotherapy, group therapy, or change in the social milieu in addition to chemical medication.

In order to understand the tranquilizers, it is important to understand the placebo effect. No therapist can avoid this effect, whether he gives a truly active medication or an inert and harmless one like a sugar tablet. The therapist is bound to project his opinions and hopes into the treatment he prescribes; and his patients, even the dull ones, are bound to react to this psychic element, sometimes quite as much as to the activity inherent in the treatment. A number of studies have shown that physicians who like tranquilizers have the best results with them and that those who put a higher value on psychotherapy get less successful results with the drugs.

The placebo effect is no insignificant item. The administration of a placebo to one group of subjects increased their appetite and pep for as many as twenty days following the administration of the harmless substance, and in some cases it nearly doubled the subject's ordinary amount of these characteristics. In some pain-killing tests, placebos almost match the effect of aspirin. A group of patients with various kinds of musculoskeletal pain were relieved 40 percent of the time by a placebo, and a placebo brought relief to one-third of others suffering from the extreme pains of cancer, angina, or severe headaches.

If one looks carefully through the medical literature, this

same placebo effect can be sensed about tranquilizers. With the advent of a new tranquilizer (and there are now several hundred), its usefulness in a great variety of conditions is widely extolled, but as the months go by, there gradually appear reports that the effectiveness of this particular tranquilizer has been reduced astronomically. In fact, there is a joke among psychiatrists that one should keep his ears open for the latest tranquilizer and use it quickly while it is still working.

Quite recently, a group of scientists who were disturbed by the tranquilizer reports appearing in their journals set up an experiment to test the tests, so to speak. They used the usual casual techniques plus the most scrupulous of scientific methods, and analyzed their data in the various ways, careful and careless, of other researchers. Two substances were tested, one described only as a new tranquilizer, NIMH–Jan. 4057, the other as a new energizer, NIMH–Mar. 2056. Hospital staff personnel and 120 patients were told only that this was a detailed clinical investigation for the National Institute of Mental Health. Half the patients took the pills, and half made up the control group.

Using the uncontrolled and subjective methods of so many studies, the research team found that data provided by patients, psychiatrists, and nurses showed that 53 to 80 percent of the patients benefited. Using the control groups, they found that the tranquilizer provided temporary improvement, whereas the energizers did not. Quite a difference—merely as the result of scientific research method.

But most important, both groups were taking placebos all the time—inert compounds that could have produced the reported improvement only by suggestion, involvement in a new experiment, change of attitude on the part of staff and/or patient, or some other nonchemical factor. No tranquilizer or energizer was given to anyone.

Another dramatic example of the danger of assuming that

drugs work only organically: It has been common in studies on the effectiveness of tranquilizers to use the patient as his own control; that is, if a patient is given drug A and improves, gets worse when A is stopped, and improves when A is started again, it is assumed that drug A is effective. But a new drug and a placebo were given to two different groups with chronic and severe schizophrenia. Using as a criterion of improvement the amount of soiling done by the patients, experimenters demonstrated that even chronically regressed patients improved when the placebo was given and got worse when it was withdrawn. There was no significant difference between results from the placebo and from the chemical.

This is not to say that the tranquilizers are useless (however useless some of the research may be). There is no doubt that potent tranquilizers like chlorpromazine have made extremely disturbed patients more manageable and have simplified hospital care. The true extent of their effect is difficult to judge, however, because while the tranquilizers have been in use, there has been great emphasis on hospital treatment of psychiatric patients. From Finland comes a comparison of patients admitted to hospitals between 1933 and 1935 and patients admitted between 1953 and 1955. All were schizophrenic and rated on such categories as degree of illness and response to therapy. In the more recent group, there was a much greater incidence of milder forms of disturbance and marked differences in the symptoms. Far better social recovery characterized the patients of the 1950's. For example, 35 percent in the 1930's were, during the four years following their discharge from the hospital, permanent hospital inmates, whereas only 5 percent of the later group were hospitalized in the equivalent period, three of them by decision of the court. Such figures would seem to make an attractive case for the tranquilizers. But tranquilizers were not introduced into the mental hospitals of Finland until late in 1954!

A single schizophrenic and his family can illustrate the complexity of judging chemicals and mind. John, the schizophrenic patient, spoke very little, and most of what he said consisted of two sentences: "I don't know," and "Mental illness is all a matter of physics and chemistry." The first had some justification because for years his parents had undercut anything else he said. The second he had heard his mother say, and so he considered it safe to repeat. Some months after family psychotherapy started, John began to show considerable improvement. The staff attributed this to the fact that his parents had begun to talk about their own relationships, thus, so to speak, taking the heat off him.

But the mother discovered that the hospital staff had put John on a new tranquilizer about this time, and not unnaturally she claimed that the drug, not the therapy, had caused the improvement. The dosage was small, so small as to seem unable to account for the change, but there was no proof. Then, one day, a nurse going through John's bedside table, found a huge mound of tranquilizer capsules that he had been saving over the months. He hadn't swallowed one.

Another time, John reacted violently to his ward doctor's tendency to forget promises. When the therapist connected this extreme behavior with his parents' tendency to do the same, John got angry, cursed, and called him crazy and dangerous. At the next family session, the therapist brought up the topic, and John's immediate response was, "Mental health is all a matter of physics."

"I agree with him that it's all a matter of physics," said his mother, but all attempts to get her to clarify her meaning were virtually useless. Everything ended in a vague statement, "Well, you know what you read in the newspapers."

Moral: Don't believe everything you read. No tranquilizer affects a schizophrenic as insulin affects a diabetic.

CHAPTER 6

IN THE MIDDLE OF THE MILIEU

"WEDDING PSYCHOSIS"—a complex of very disturbing schizophrenia-like symptoms—is not uncommon among Moslem women who live in Algeria. Their marriages, still arranged for them by their elders, are many times forced against their wishes, and often bride and groom are not so much as introduced before the beginning of the ceremony. Futhermore, according to trained and objective observers, the older women who participate in the wedding—grandmother, mother, sisters, or aunts—take a sadistic pleasure in encouraging the appearance of the typical symptoms that they themselves have had as brides and since recovered from. Having been victims, they want others to be victimized in the same way.

The appearance of such a mental disorder follows none of the rules of genetics, and it seems highly unlikely that a particular gene can be held responsible, although observing one of these women without knowing the situation, even a professional might diagnose schizophrenia. But if he knew the culture's traditions, he would hardly be surprised to learn that the more the bride knows about the liberal marriage customs of Western Europe and the United States, the more likely she is to develop wedding psychosis. Not unnaturally, the disorder occurs most frequently in the Westernized Algerian cities.

Do societies—or the conflicts between societies—produce mental disorder? If it can be shown that different cultures produce different forms of disturbance—different "diseases" —the argument against heredity is strengthened. One does not inherit cultural pressures by way of the genes. In recent years, interest in this theory has grown tremendously, and a great many studies have been made, some exploring wide cultural territories, others restricted to small, compact segments of subcultures. Regrettably this seems to be an area of very little interest to the popular journalist. For some reason, what appears to be exciting news to many professionals, avid for what few reports they can find in their technical literature, never reaches the public press. The Moslem women may be of not too much concern to the American layman, but the overall pattern that begins to emerge from these cross-cultural studies is of great importance and deserves more and better exposure.

Of course, a few psychiatrists, dropping in for brief visits to various groups scattered about the world, have concluded that mental disorders are much the same everywhere—and therefore genetic. Their remarks raise the hackles of anthropologists, who realize the enormous difficulty of judging the behavior of one culture and comparing it with another, as well as sorting out the biases created by hospitality, the eagerness to have the visitor see what he is looking for. More and more, psychiatrist and anthropologist work as a team to overcome these obstacles.

It is not surprising, of course, that mental disorders have something in common in all lands, because all people are biological creatures, and any number of human brains can give rise to only a finite number of patterns. On the other hand, it is not surprising that differences exist because most authorities agree that culture obviously has its effects. The big question: How much?

Some interesting and suggestive preliminary discoveries have been made by a group of Canadian scholars even as they themselves admit the difficulty of collecting worldwide information. While all psychiatrists everywhere are agreed on social and emotional withdrawal, hallucinations and delusions, and flatness of emotional reaction as typical schizophrenic symptoms, certain other symptoms are associated with particular cultures. For example, catatonic stereotypy appears frequently among the Japanese, but not often elsewhere; catatonic excitement and catatonic rigidity are seen in Indian patients, but seldom occur in Europe and America. Even the delusions of schizophrenics vary from group to group: Asians evidence more delusional jealousy, Christians have far more delusions of destruction than non-Christians, and they have more religious delusions than do Moslems, who have more than Hindus, Buddhists, Taoists, and Shintoists. Homicidal trends are most common in Africans, suicidal in Japanese (as they are among African and Japanese in general, not just African and Japanese schizophrenics).

In more generalized terms, a preponderance of Western, "literate" schizophrenia seems to be dominated by the paranoid form, whereas nonliterate peoples tend to have more cases of conversion hysteria (that is, a physical symptom, perhaps paralysis of the arm, that is caused by psychological conflict rather than bodily injury) and a schizophrenia that responds to witch doctoring plus community support as paranoid conditions do not. Thus the differences do appear within what is usually considered a "single" disorder, and the variations in the category *schizophrenia* complicate the already complex picture.

Sometimes the very question of what is normal and what abnormal plagues the investigator of cultures. Assuming that he is the product of a literate society, how is he to make wise evaluation and hard and fast decisions about a nonliterate group whose standards are so far removed from his? Even the explanations of basic natural phenomena will differ, not to mention the subtler distinctions inherent in human life. Within his literate society, magic, for example, has adherents whose degree of belief varies to such an extent that what one patient says to a psychiatrist may reflect his usual thinking (perhaps about black cats) and be quite unexceptional for him, whereas a second patient (always a cat fancier) may say the same thing and thereby show great disturbance of mind and severe delusions.

Now, in a nonliterate culture, where similar magical thinking is used to explain occurrences for which even the black-cat patient knows the scientific explanation, how much more difficult to distinguish between cultural beliefs and delusional thinking. The researcher must know both society and patient in order to come up with data, diagnosis, or even tentative hypothesis.

A fascinating difference of schizophrenia symptoms occurs even within the very small country of Ghana (population 6½ million, or less than New York City), where belief in witchcraft is widespread among healthy and disturbed alike. But a schizophrenic patient from the primitive northern region may hallucinate ghosts and fairies, whereas one from the industrial south complains that he is controlled by a radio or some other modern mechanism. On the other hand, one particular group, the Ashantis, whose subculture is intensively organized politically, tend to have delusions of great wealth and claim royal birth or relationship to powerful chiefs.

Because the larger number of all disturbed patients come from the south, which is the most progressive and Westernized region, and because their hospital admission rate increased from 3 in 100,000 population to 10 within a thirteen-year period (a truly startling increase), it has suggested that schizophrenia is directly related to environmental changes and the personality's inability to handle them.

More support for this position comes from men working

with Japanese patients. Today it is impossible not to have some inkling of the tremendous changes that have occurred within this particular culture, where a highly structured feudal hierarchy had dominated every aspect of life for centuries. Duty and obedience, dominance and submission, discipline and control had characterized society until the end of the nineteenth century when, gradually, industrialization and liberalization began to appear. The industrial boss became a father figure. Religion became worship of the state, and family feeling became the cult of the emperor. Japanese invincibility and Japan's destiny as the ruler of all Asia were of paramount importance. Suddenly, the end of World War II, defeat, occupation, female suffrage, strong trade unions, the humanization of the emperor—chaos. Many young Japanese, faced with this disruption of tradition, a ruined economy, and much unemployment, showed their shock and anxiety in antisocial behavior (sex crimes, drug addition, suicide), while others looked for a new authority figure in Communism or the American occupation troops.

One of the second group was Ken Wada. He was the eldest son of a self-made and very successful businessman. His mother was an unhappy woman whose childhood had been spent wandering the countryside with a divorced mother and her professional-storyteller lover and whose marriage had been arranged by her family. Ken was shy and introverted as a boy. Above average intellectually, he nevertheless did poorly in school, stuttered, and had a peculiar habit of sniffing his fingers. During his school days in Korea, he joined a group striking against their Japanese teachers and was suspended. This rebellion and its punishment made him skeptical of everything, nervous, and depressed; and one of a long series of family quarrels resulted, his father blaming his mother for Ken's flaunting of authority. But he did begin his college studies before going off to war and made a close friend, Takeo, who was to be even more important to him later.

Very early in the fighting, Ken was taken prisoner by the Russians, and as a result, at the war's end, found that his Siberian education greatly enhanced his position with a college Communist group. Takeo had also become an ardent Communist, and the relationship between the two grew closer and homosexually tinged, although Takeo had had a girl, making Ken feel envious and inferior.

A year later, Takeo was admitted to the Tokyo National University. Like many Japanese at the time, he also became more conservative politically. Ken, not wanting to be separated from him, decided to change schools, too; but, reluctant to change his political position so drastically, he began to feel the conflict between friendship and belief. His Communist friends sensed his doubts, and his days as kingpin were over.

At the same time, his father objected strenuously to further education. Ken's mother sided with her son, and during the resulting family crises she became so depressed as to take to her bed for nearly a year. The housekeeper brought in to cope with this emergency provided Ken's first heterosexual experience—unsatisfactory, not surprisingly, because he proved to be partially impotent. Takeo urged him to brothels, only increasing his symptoms and giving him the idea that he had a venereal disease that was malignant.

Having failed his entrance examination for the National University, Ken went elsewhere, financially supported by his younger brothers because his father refused to condone further education. Thus Ken carried with him his guilt about both his mother's condition and his brothers' expenses.

Takeo was busy with finals, and Ken, lonely and disappointed, asked his mother to arrange a marriage. She produced the daughter of a professor of medicine, but even after the formal engagement, Ken wavered. So when Takeo criticized the girl during a summer-vacation visit, Ken first quarreled with him and then broke the engagement.

By fall, Ken's symptoms were more acute, and by spring, he was announcing to a classmate: "Everybody, except me, belongs to 'society.' 'Society' is against me. The only other person who doesn't belong is 'Mummy.' " He began to shout, "I want a Mummy! I want a Mummy!" His friend tried to calm him and advised him to say "sweetheart" or "girl" instead of "Mummy." But the word "Mummy" had, for Ken, the indescribable sense of what he wanted. He wanted not a sweetheart or a girl friend, but a Mummy.

Barely passing his exams, he was graduated, took an insurance job, propped a book up to pretend work, and knew that his condition called for help. Despite his family's casual attitude toward his problem, he presented himself at a clinic. His complaints involved being called a Communist, being persecuted by a detective, and having venereal disease; and his diagnosis was schizophrenia, with hypochondria and delusions of persecution.

Ken Wada was caught between two traditions, although unlike the conflicts created by industrialization in Ghana, his conflicts were more clearly centered within his family situation. His mother acted as Japanese mothers have acted for centuries, lavishing affection on her son in the hope of getting from him the love and sympathy that her husband could not give because of her inferior position in the family. At the same time, Ken's mother was not a traditional Japanese woman; her relatively independent and wandering girlhood and her own mother's broken marriage gave her no pattern of submissive wife to follow.

Outside the family, social change and resistance permeated Ken's surroundings, so that with his mother's encouragement and his brothers' willingness to break with tradition and defy their father's wishes, Ken could reject the role of eldest son as it had been played by his ancestors. But he could not do so without strong feelings of conflict and guilt. Challenging his father's authority, he also rejected his own masculinity and his country. His negation of so much of such great importance made him one of the "psychic casualties" of sudden social change.

Immigration provides another example of the psychological results of shifting cultures, for migrant groups are found to suffer from collective anxiety, whatever their origin, race, or nationality. In Australia, for example, immigrants have many times the number of psychoses that the native-born do. Twenty-seven percent of hospitalized schizophrenics have recently arrived, although the percentage of immigrants in the population is nowhere nearly so high. Adjustment to new living conditions and the prejudices of the native-born seem to create the problems in Australia, as they have been found to do elsewhere.

Witness the situation in Okinawan, South African, and Indian cultures, which produce fewer depressive disorders than European cultures do, a fact explained by the longer, self-demand nursing period common among these people. In addition, the Okinawans have very few behavior disorders and very little psychosomatic disease. Interestingly, however, Okinawan immigrants to Hawaii show a high number of psychoses, higher than any other ethnic groups in the Islands, even though these immigrants use the same mothering methods. But evidence of their impoverished social condition shows up again and again in the content of their psychoses and their personality problems.

In a more encouraging vein is the word from Formosa that although second-generation Chinese (that is, the native-born descendants of the original Chinese immigrants) have the same proportion of psychoses as do members of other cultures, they seem to have fewer nonpsychotic mental disorders. The infrequent occurrence of psychopathic personalities is ascribed to Chinese emphasis on filial piety, conformity to the traditional social pattern, and the high degree of tolerance of deviant behavior typical of their family structure. The scarcity of alcoholism is attributed to the mutual dependence of this particular family system and to the fact that drinking celebrates interpersonal relationships instead of emphasizing the relaxation of inhibitions, as it does in the Western cultures. Here, some parts of the centuries-old tradition seem able to survive with beneficial rather than disastrous results.

But what would happen if rapidly shifting environment, cultural pressures, and immigration were combined? Sometimes, the unexpected. Take, for example, Miss L., a young Chinese woman, the second oldest of six children. Her father and older brother were Confucian, her mother Buddhist, and she and the other four children Christians—in itself a sign of change in the once stable Chinese system. During her childhood, her father was a government official. Although she was shy, lonely, and, by her own account, somewhat spoiled, and despite the many moves necessitated by her father's work, she did well in school. Then came the Japanese invasion and more moves. The family was often separated and had many a narrow escape. Once, during World War II, Miss L. herself led a group of children through a Japanese blockade to free territory.

After the war, Miss L. went to college on the Chinese mainland, which by then was virtually dominated by the Communists. Having taught for a year in a nearby elementary school—avoiding politics for the most part—she returned to free territory to live with her parents and take charge of the music program in the high school.

Two aspects of her life led her to come to the United States. First, she felt inadequately trained for her new teaching position. Second, her loneliness led her to write to a former fellow student, four years younger than she, who was in an American college. Earlier, she had felt "like a mother" to him, but now she fell in love by correspondence. At no time had she any kind of sexual experience: "I could be weak like that, but I try to be strong."

Not accepted by the young man's school, Miss L. went to a woman's college and had no chance to see him until spring vacation. Somehow, in person, things did not work out; there were misunderstandings about minor points, the man offered her a badly needed loan, and they quarreled bitterly. He announced that he was going to marry an American girl. One of her reasons for being in America was gone, and she returned to classes feeling completely abandoned.

Her college work itself presented problems, for her English was so meager that she had to take notes and write papers in Chinese and translate later. For the first few months, however, she did well. Then finances became troublesome, and although friends were glad to make loans and gifts, she was desperate when she could not reciprocate in the style demanded by old Chinese custom. An outbreak of stealing in the dormitory convinced her that she was suspect as an impoverished foreigner.

A paper on the Sino-Japanese war was upsetting: "It made me sound warlike—but you can't forget a thing like that." Besides, she had mentioned a sister who was a surgeon in Red China. The girls would feel that she was a Communist. She was sure of it when, after a friend had looked casually through her books, she herself discovered for the first time that one of them had been printed on the Chinese mainland.

The next Christmas was particularly difficult. Miss L. was terribly homesick, the mail from home was late, and she began to worry about her family. Then came a music recital and still more problems. The middle-aged, unmarried professor in charge had included a song that referred to a Christmas rose. The year before Miss L. had sent out cards decorated with a rose and an affectionate message—in Chinese characters.

Therefore, she assumed that the professor (who, she admitted, reminded her of her father) had misunderstood her greeting and was telling her by means of the song that he returned her love. Besides, she thought that he was loved by an older woman. This group of delusions led to the idea that everyone thought she was married. Her work suffered, she became withdrawn, and she told her friends: "They're laughing and talking about me. The atmosphere is entirely changed."

When she had to be hospitalized, she was friendly but reserved. Improvement was rapid, and she was able to complete her course that spring. But the next year, the severe symptoms reappeared, and despite a second quick recovery, she was returned to free territory in China. There she has functioned well ever since, without any medical help whatsoever.

It is hardly necessary or possible to try to sort out the precise factors that may have precipitated Miss L.'s mental disturbance, but the stresses and strains, beginning very early in her life, are perfectly obvious. Gross environmental changes followed one another in quick succession, and, in fact, she seems to have had the kind of life that leads one to say, "No wonder the poor thing broke down," rather than "She must have inherited bad genes"—proving that folk sayings are not always too wrong.

But what, more specifically and scientifically, do the cultural factors do to the genetic hypothesis? For a number of reasons, Singapore provides useful information. Assuming that 1 percent of patients admitted to public hospitals are diagnosed as schizophrenic (as they are elsewhere) and assuming the genetic theory that schizophrenia is a recessive disorder, 10 to 15 percent of the parents of these patients should be schizophrenic, too. These percentages can be arrived at in Singapore, but the actual situation is so different as to make them meaningless.

First, the Indian population of the city, on a per capita basis, has twice as many cases as the Chinese group, and the Chinese have twice as many as the Malays. These differences could be accounted for in terms of the genetic stock of each of the three groups, if schizophrenia is inherited. But the first-born son of an Indian family is by far the most susceptible to schizophrenia of any member of any race or any age group in the city. (In fact, he has twelve times the chance of being hospitalized with a diagnosis of schizophrenia as a Malay female does.) And even within one's own ethnic group, specific genes are not reserved for the eldest sons.

Second, among the parents of these particular patients a large number of cases can be found—but only because Indian women over forty have far more disturbances than the girls of twenty or less. If, instead of calculating the statistics for "parents," one separates the data into "mother" and "father," the usual genetic pattern breaks down. Indian males and females have about the same number of cases of schizophrenia, but the males have them early, the females late. As a result, the 15 percent figure for parents of patients is heavily weighted with mothers. Geneticists do not commonly make the distinction, assuming that parents contribute equally to a child's genetic structure and that schizophrenics divide 7½ percent and 7½ percent. But studies other than genetic have found no such equal division, as we shall see in Chapter 9.

From the Singapore material, two other kinds of data are worth mentioning. Under the age of thirty-five, schizophrenia is twice as common among members of large family groups as it is among single persons and those living in *Kongsi*, or social clubs. In the simplest terms, one can imagine the pressures exerted on certain young adults by a complex cultural group like the large, close family. On the other hand, compared to single individuals and members of *Kongsi*, astonishingly few members of the large families are hospitalized for mental disturbances caused by such physical disorders as arteriosclerosis; the family is prepared to take care of its aged, relieving them of the pressures that they might feel if they were unattached and had to continue working to eat. The importance of social pressure also appears in the statistical breakdown by occupation of the mentally disturbed. For example, among the Malay, the skilled craftsmen have six times as many first admissions to hospitals for mental disorders as do the messengers and office boys. Therefore, it may also be misleading to report "patients" or "parents" without also reporting socioeconomic level—but more of that in Chapter 7.

The great variations revealed in the Singapore figures, with their subtle and fascinating implications, could easily be lost by lumping together nationalities, sexes, and ages. Typically, a geneticist picks the hundred patients who, on their first admission to the hospital, had been diagnosed as schizophrenic, and then examines parents, siblings, and other blood relatives. Reporting, for example, that 10 percent of the parents were schizophrenics, whereas the average rate is 1 percent, he establishes a recessive hereditary trend. But the parents are probably between forty and fifty years old, and he may perhaps be ascertaining only that the incidence of mental disorder is high in this age group, a group old enough to have sons and daughters in their early twenties.

A more adequate standard of measurement would be the historically accurate number of cases in which one or the other parent has a condition similar to the patient's and at the same age—that is, a parent who had schizophrenia at twenty and whose child subsequently developed schizophrenia at twenty. When a woman of forty is disturbed and so, simultaneously, is her son of twenty, we are on shaky ground if we assume that the disorder is the same and has been passed on by the genes. Perhaps, in actuality, those personality traits and cultural pressures that resulted in her depression with its paranoid features (a condition likely to be labeled schizophrenia when one is counting blood relatives for a specific purpose, but not necessarily so) produced the kind of relationship with her offspring that made him schizophrenic (and truly so). This possibility we shall explore in Chapters 8 and 9. Meanwhile, the effects of culture and environment on seemingly cut and dried statistics may profitably be added to the dearth of specific information about genetic factors and the fruitless quests of the biochemists.

CHAPTER 7

CLOSER TO HOME

EVEN THOUGH it is usually more difficult to examine and assess objectively our own way of life, culture and environment less remote than Singapore must be taken into consideration. Perhaps the job can be made easier by beginning with a small segment or subculture: the Hutterites, a religious group who live in Montana, North and South Dakota, and also in two provinces of Canada—not too far away geographically, but in many respects quite outside the current of American culture.

The Hutterites form an Anabaptist sect, founded in 1528 in Switzerland, although at the end of the eighteenth century they migrated to Russia. Between 1874 and 1877, the entire group, only a few hundred souls, left Russia for the United States because the Czarist government was attempting to incorporate them into the Russian system, whose military service in particular they found distasteful.

The Hutterites live for eternal religious salvation, and believe it is achieved by their way of life. They are rural, cooperative, communal livers who do without most of the conveniences of the modern world. The community buys clothes, doles out pocket money, and takes care of virtually all other needs, including medical ones. Because men are not sent away from the communities for any kind of training, such professionals as teachers and physicians are imported from the outside and paid by the colony. Women are allowed to retire from hard labor at forty-five and men somewhat later. The sect takes care of its own.

A remarkable opportunity to study and observe in the Hutterite communities, which now have a total population of about 8,000, gave a psychiatrist and a sociologist, working together, a great amount of data on the relationship between a subculture and its mental disorders. By a meticulous process of screening with personal interviews, physical examinations, and psychological examinations, the researchers identified 53 psychotics, 69 neurotics, 20 epileptics, 51 mental defectives, and 6 cases of personality disorders in the colonies. Surprisingly, 74 percent of the psychotics were diagnosed as having "manic-depressive psychoses." All were in the depressed phase; apparently a manic, or excited, period was virtually unknown. This percentage is at a sharp variance with the usual mental-hospital statistics; there one finds 20 or more schizophrenics to 1 manic depressive.

In addition, only 8 Hutterites had ever been hospitalized for their mental disorders, and these 8 included depressives who had electroshock treatments and rather brief psychotic episodes. Most of the depressives recovered under the devoted care of their own untrained brethren. The few schizophrenics seemed largely of the paranoid type, and they too were cared for within the communities, treated as ill, and not shunned by the other members. In fact, great pressure to recover was put on them by everyone because of the emphasis of their religious beliefs on willpower.

The culture of the Hutterites can readily be linked to depressive symptoms and their formation. The emphasis on guilt, the restrictions, the lack of encouragement to express feelings, and other characteristics of their faith and their community system all fit what is known about the formation of depressive patterns in general. Given the data, the seemingly lopsided percentages become not only clear but rationally unavoidable. Probably no other work has so clearly demonstrated the relationship between a culture and a particular form of psychosis.

Except for the Hutterites, people living in urban areas seem to have received a disproportionate amount of attention (perhaps because the psychiatrists and sociologists live there), for there is no indication that country dwellers have fewer emotional problems. The data that have emerged from the cities are interesting, if sometimes contradictory. For example, the relationship between socioeconomic class and mental disorder has been questioned for many years, perhaps as a result of the old association of inherited poverty, disease, and insanity with "inferior" peoples.

A survey in Chicago concerned only with hospital-admission figures proved a consistent pattern: schizophrenics came from the socioeconomically low districts in the center of the city by as many as 10 to 1. Two theories have been offered to explain this phenomenon, the *drift hypothesis* and the *breeder hypothesis*. Adherents of the first believe that the emotionally ill tend to move downward into the lower levels as they become more disturbed. This hypothesis would seem to have some features in common with the genetic-defect theory and with the older ideas about mental disorder. The crazy man will look only a little better than the ape; he will be ragged and dirty and unkempt; he won't be one of the "nice people." Like seek out like—and hence the lower classes.

The breeder hypothesis, on the other hand, assumes that the neighborhood itself creates schizophrenia in susceptible individuals, an idea reminiscent of older Utopian schemes for ridding the world of all evils by clearing away the slums.

An interesting variation, based on more extensive though not yet conclusive information, involves the effect of social class on the form of mental disorder, the attitudes toward it, and the subsequent therapeutic history of the patient. The men who have been most closely associated with this thesis, A. B. Hollingshead and F. C. Redlich, feel that schizophrenia may be more prevalent among the lower socioeconomic groups because the environment there during the child's first five or six important formative years does not provide well-defined individuals and roles within the family, good models of personal interaction, and sufficient opportunity to master gradually the complexities of growing up in the world. On the upper levels, they find more evidence of, for example, obsessive-compulsive disorders (that is, conditions in which the patient repeats a specific act, or feels compelled to go over and over a single idea or a specific aspect of his environment).

In a wealthy middle-class suburb, however, the form, amount, and degree of mental disorders are not seemingly different from those elsewhere. In Crestwood Heights (as this sample community was called in the book about its life, psychological and otherwise), the residents know little of poverty or economic deprivation. Instead their emotional problems seem to be related to ambitions, upward mobility, success, and other positive factors. This association would not be expected if mental disorder is a defect, caused by a defective gene. Or if it is argued that successful, ambitious people are driven by genetic factors, it should be difficult to recommend the eugenic practices that are discussed in Chapter 11 because those people who have new and original ideas, get things done, and generally make the innovations and improvements in our culture would be automatically suspect.

The stereotype of the successful businessman taking pills for his ulcers or his high blood pressure, both often associated with "nerves" and success, is common enough. In fact, during the early tranquilizer craze, popping pills was almost obligatory among the status seekers. In this particular field, epoch-making work has been done by two doctors, L. E. Hinkle and H. G. Wolff, who began by studying blood pressure in groups of very different individuals: skilled American-born workingmen, semiskilled American-born workingmen, Chinese graduate students and professional people, Hungarian refugees, recent graduates of American colleges, and young managerial employees with high-school diplomas. They found that a fourth of the members of each group had about half the episodes of illness, not just higher blood pressure but all kinds of physical illnesses.

Furthermore, they discovered that new episodes of illness tended to occur in these people in clusters that had no fixed length and developed at no special time of life. These "clusters of illness" appeared in four-fifths of the sick or stressed members of each group, with a wide variety of symptoms that arose from various causes. They were more likely to occur when the individual felt that his life situation was particularly demanding, threatening, and/or frustrating, whatever socioeconomic group he belonged to. How the individual saw his own situation was important, not some external measurement of how difficult the situation really was.

Thus, Wolff and Hinkle have demonstrated that individuals do not have a specific psychosomatic illness; rather, they respond to stressful situations with a variety of illnesses. Hypertension and peptic ulcers are no more or no less likely to occur in the poorly adapted person than are lobar pneumonia and fractures of the long bones, regardless of the stereotypes; the vice-president with ulcers and the office boy with the perpetual sniffle may not be so far apart as they think.

One important question raised by this work involves the role of inherited constitution. If psychosomatic diseases are thought of as discrete entities—for example, thyroid disease, peptic ulcer, asthma—then it is easy for physicians to feel that afflicted individuals have genes that make them specifically vulnerable in these organ systems. But this research seems to have demonstrated that the individual who feels himself under unusual pressure may respond with many types of illness. It is difficult to postulate a gene that accounts for an increased number of broken bones, and the very specificity that other genetic diseases show is lacking if one is forced to postulate "general vulnerability to illness."

Racial origins made no more difference than social class in this particular study. Whether Chinese, Hungarian, or American-born, the more ambitious, upwardly mobile, and other-directed person tends to fall into the category of the more frequently ill. These people showed a particular interest in social "causes," whereas the healthy sample had to be described as socially insulated, in the sense that they had no deep ties to anybody or anything. Again, are the eugenicists willing to select against this "unhealthy" group?

Although our concern is not primarily care and cure, a discussion of culture and environment would be incomplete without a look at the results they produce after mental disturbance is an acknowledged and diagnosed fact. And because some of the results cast grave doubts on the genetic theory, they properly belong to our story. Take, for example, a newspaper interview granted by the superintendent of a large municipal institution in surburban Stockholm, who decided that some of his mental patients might do better if they were allowed to summer on the Italian Riviera. Of 50 patients, all had been in the hospital from ten to twenty-eight years, and during that time, some had not spoken a complete sentence. After the experiment, the doctor decided that it confirmed his belief that "a dramatic, positive change in environment" is an antidote to the hospital syndrome. He said in a newspaper interview that patients receiving electroshock therapy would continue their treatments away from the hospital the next time such a trip was arranged—"if there is a next time. I will soon be 65 and eligible for a holiday myself." Of interest is the fact that 8 patients with hebephrenia, paranoia, or catatonia, all hospitalized more than fifteen years, were permanently discharged after the group returned to Stockholm.

The interview is depressing insofar as it proves that a little ingenuity in the care of the mental patient is still news. But it is cheering to know that a long-time medical superintendent, just before his own retirement, has the courage to try something different and see that it works. How often does our preoccupation with genetics, biochemistry, and physiology keep us from thinking up simple, yet effective measures for mental-patient care? Surely the genes are not altered by a trip to the Riviera. Nor are they altered by hospitalization, although hospitalization can very easily affect some of the factors studied by the geneticist, as we have seen.

That an unusual and special environment can produce misleading changes has recently been demonstrated by three ordinary, nonpsychotic men between the ages of twenty-one and thirty-six. For fourteen days, each was put in an isolation room with built-in toilet facilities, food chamber, and air conditioner, the only furniture being a mattress. The men wore goggles to reduce light, special gloves to minimize tactile stimulation, and ear equipment that produced a constant noise without tune or harmony. If they tried to sing, hum, or indulge in any other vocal activity, the experimenter remonstrated, but their movements were not restricted. In addition, they were under constant observation by closed circuit television.

Before the experiment and on the seventh, tenth, twelfth, and fourteenth days of isolation, electroencephalograms (EEG) were made, and each man showed a progressive decrease in the number of waves in the alpha range (that is, fewer than the normal 8 or 10 per second that come largely from the frontal lobes). This decrease lasted for some time after the men left the isolation chamber, and in each case the EEG was abnormal a week later. In addition, all reported decided lessening of motivation that lasted from three to eight days, and all showed a marked disinclination to exert physical or mental effort of any kind. For our purposes, these three experimental subjects are important primarily because EEG changes have so often been reported in hospitalized schizophrenics. No one has ever considered that these changes might be the result of the hospital environment rather than something inherent in the biological structure of the mentally disturbed.

Another and perhaps the most gratifying test of environmental influence is improvement of the patient, and here a study of a group of World War II veterans gives us information. Diagnosed as schizophrenic during their military service, half were hospitalized and half were seen as outpatients, a fact that proved nothing about the degree of their disturbance, as might be expected. For example, such severe symptoms as hallucinations and delusions were found in 20 percent of the outpatient group and in 37 percent of the hospitalized group. On the basis of the Wechsler Intelligence Test, it appeared that those in either group who had the best intellectual endowment also had greater potential for rehabilitation, but there was no evidence that intellectual endowment provided any protection against developing schizophrenia.

The men's ages at enlistment had ranged from seventeen to fifty-one, with an average of twenty-three. Their length of service was from three to one hundred and twenty-three months, with an average of about thirty-three months, so prolonged exposure to obvious stress did not reveal a significant pattern. Whether or not the individuals went overseas did not matter; and the mere fact of separation from familial and environmental supports seemed to be the important thing. Neither group was distinguished by having a majority who had shown personality disturbances before their breakdowns, and there were no marked differences in terms of family histories of mental disorders. If the genetic factor was important, one would expect the patients who stayed out of the hospital to show fewer foreshadowings of disturbance and to have healthier family histories, but such was not the case.

The most important single factor in adjustment was family support. Most of the outpatients lived with their families, and the best adjusted of the group had families who were better informed about mental health and more insightful and optimistic about the patients' condition than did the other veterans.

Within the hospital, the effectiveness of interpersonal support is emphasized by the influence of visitors on recovery. In one instance, patients who entertained had an average hospital stay of about seven and a half years, whereas the average patient was there between sixteen and seventeen years. Twelve months after a three-week comparison of the visited and a chance sampling of patients (who were otherwise comparable in age, sex, and so on), 50 of the visited had been discharged and only 21 of the others.

On discharge, however, the direction of the patients' progress is still variable. Most of those in one group who tried to return to parents or spouse were back in the hospital within three months. Yet, getting along best outside were a group living successfully with a spouse. If the marriage can take it, the patient has a good chance; if it cannot, he is better off living in a single room.

Thus, not only the hospital environment—both the physical plant and the human relationships—but also the world to which the person returns can determine the course of his disorder. Professional and layman alike should consider both aspects of the situation with a seriousness that would be unnecessary if the pessimism inherent in older concepts of the emotions were justified.

But such concern is not easy to come by. It seems to be very difficult for the average person to appreciate the effect of psychosocial forces upon him. We are all so accustomed to our usual niches that we have no reason to think about them in terms of their influence on us. Actually, each of us plays a number of different parts (which the sociologist calls "roles") in our daily lives, usually so automatically fitted into the culture and our surroundings that they go on without our awareness. But these roles are not without their effects, and the emotional impact of a change in roles can result in peculiar mental and emotional impressions. A simple example can illustrate their importance.

As a teaching method, I often play the part of a patient while a psychiatrist-in-training interviews me. During such an interview, when I was very much involved in being a depressed patient, the young man made a rather meaningful slip of the tongue. My mind went momentarily blank; I was blocked and unable to continue my patient role; and I broke out laughing. Obviously, his slip put me back in my usual role of the psychiatrist who studies and utilizes such slips, instead of my adopted role of patient. Yet the mental experience, that is, the blankness and blocking, is not to be ignored even though it was momentary and in this case unimportant. If one were constantly exposed to conflicts of roles, then blocking and confusion would be frequent and eventually perhaps permanent.

In another instance, I was playing the part of the patient and, when the psychiatrist playing the therapist asked me if I had been in the war, I said angrily, "It wasn't in Korea." My idea, as patient, was that he was supposed to know that I had been in World War II; I expected him to remember my history. At this moment, however, the psychiatrist playing my father leaned forward and said, "But Burt, you were never in Korea," and before I could recover from this puzzling remark, the female psychiatrist playing my mother backed him up by saying, "Yes, Burt, you were never in Korea. What do you mean?" Again, I experienced that momentary but extreme blocking and blankness, and then I could almost feel what it might be like to be the son of that father and mother. I did not expect any such response to my remark—a confused negation of what had been said that forced me out of my role. But some families behave that way constantly, providing the kind of atmosphere and environment for their children that we shall see in Chapters 8 and 9. They confuse, negate, and all too often seriously disturb the child's natural and necessary learning processes. If they do not transmit the culture to him in a clear-cut way, then his idea of what role he is to play may become confused. In some families, it is left totally unspecified. In others, the parents are in conflict over it, and he is caught between them with contradictory pictures of what he is and what he is to become. Ultimately, especially for the very young child, environment can be defined in terms of home and family, and it is there that we must look for further influences on mental health.

CHAPTER 8

FATHER, MOTHER, AND SIBLINGS

IN ONE SENSE, we have now come full circle—back to the beginnings of psychoanalysis and the new psychiatry as they originated with Freud and his school in late nineteenth-century Vienna—back to the feelings, infant feeding, toilet training, sex, and all the other shockers to Victorian morality—back to the family. However biological the basic concept of the Oedipus complex, it is first and foremost a family situation, one through which children are supposed to grow in order to become mature and mentally healthy. The Freudians, both early and contemporary, feel that lack of development before and during this crucial period means neurosis or psychosis or at least an uncomfortable emotional life. In other words, despite the emphasis that Freud put on biological sexuality, the problems that it can cause lie within the family.

But Freud and the other founding fathers of modern psychiatry, still following the outlines of medical practice, treated individual patients. No need to put a cast on Sister when Junior breaks his leg. Even Harry Stack Sullivan, who put so much emphasis on the relationship between interpersonal relations and mental health, and who very early began to explore the possibilities of using psychotherapy to treat the severely disturbed, handled the patient as a single individual.

In fact, not dealing with any member of the family except the patient was for many years one of the cardinal rules of psychoanalysis. Freud early took the position that a successful analysis meant keeping the relatives out of the picture, and in one paper he warned his colleagues about the distressing fate that awaited them if they attempted to deal with the patient's family.

Not much more than ten years ago, in a relatively isolated sanatarium, we were treating schizophrenics with psychotherapy, but we never had anything to do with their families. In those days, it was unheard of for the therapist to encounter the parents or other relatives; he always left them to the administrator. My own situation was changed by moving to a small town where it was impossible to avoid the relatives, and the results were surprising and sometimes not very pleasant. I became interested in the question of family interaction and balance—or the lack of them—which seemed most marked in the families where the schizophrenic patient was able to live at home. If he went through psychotherapy and benefited from it, any move on his part would usually produce all sorts of disruptions at home. Curiously enough, very little has been written about this topic, although people who practice psychotherapy can confirm my findings and add horror stories of their own about what happened when they undertook therapy with schizophrenics and ignored the patients' relatives. Until recently, the seriously disturbed were almost always treated in hospitals away from their relatives, and there was no occasion to examine the idea that schizophrenia could be in part an adaptive disorder that links itself to disturbance in the family itself—a situation in which change in the patient's symptoms produces feedback into the family situation.

Thus, not only have practicing therapists and research workers come to recognize that mental disturbances *arise* within a family setting. (Even geneticists must admit that most people are in some kind of family situation when the genes begin to work; where else could the patient be "taken sick"?) But some of them have also begun to consider hypotheses suggesting that family situations *cause* mental disturbances. In other words, father, mother, brothers, and sisters, if any, behave in such a way that one member of the family, either in an attempt to satisfy their needs and meet their demands or as a result of total inability to do so, is forced into the abnormal behavior that we call mental disorder. This member is singled out as "sick" and sent to the doctor, to be diagnosed as neurotic, manic-depressive, schizophrenic, or whatever. Actually, however, the behavior of the entire family must be, and must have been, abnormal in order to bring about the situation; in a sense, the family is "sick." So more and more psychiatrists and psychologists are turning their attention to the family group, the "patient" being considered only a part of the whole.

Even within the relatively few years that the idea of family disturbance has been current, several theories have been developed, modified, and, sometimes, discarded. Not long ago, for example, "momism" was the dirty word, and all the ills of mankind were laid at mother's door. Not only in the popular press, but in the scholarly journals as well, there were reports of the disastrous results of "bad mothering"—juvenile delinquency and adult criminality, mild neuroses and severe psychoses, the complete degradation of the American male, all were predicted. The "schizophrenogenic mother," she who causes her children's illnesses, was the sole culprit. Although it is true that mother has the first role, and a very important one, in relation to the child, very few experts these days would make her solely responsible for his problems.

For over ten years now, some very interesting and important family studies have been made by Theodore Lidz and his coworkers, and they are still sorting through a large number of maternal characteristics, looking for common and significant patterns. Thus far, all they can say is that some traits "recur frequently" in the mothers of disturbed children. Among them are a kind of imperviousness to what the child is trying to communicate to her, a confusion of her needs and the child's, either undue restrictiveness or an inability to set any limits at all, a low opinion of herself as a woman, and a tendency to distort situations in order to create a preconceived version of herself and her family.

This is not an attractive picture, and unfortunately it is only part of the whole, for the fathers are as frequently and as severely disturbed. In fact, Lidz believes that some of the women "would or could have been reasonably adequate mothers, had they only been unimpeded by serious marital difficulties or the demands of their disturbed husbands." Again there is no formal list of common traits among fathers, but in general they are very often insecure about their masculinity and need constant attention to build up their self-esteem. Even the domineering fathers seem to be recognized as weak and ineffectual by their families. Some are paranoid or irrational in their behavior, and their insensitivity to others is like that of many of the mothers. Often the father competes with his child, and his insecurity as a husband and father prevents his son from developing his identity as a man and his daughter as a woman.

Not surprisingly, the interaction between such parents has its effect on the children, too, so that the problem obviously becomes very much more complex, and family disorders are the result. A case in point typifies an all too frequent situation —the college student who, living away from home, has a psychotic episode. The family influence is pervasive even in absence, and in addition the patient is usually returned to the center and focus of his problems.

The patient, Jane, a nineteen-year-old college girl, had a

psychotic break six weeks before completing her junior year in college. She was transferred to my care after her first ten days of hospitalization, during which she had been diagnosed as suffering from an acute paranoid reaction. When I first saw Jane on the psychotic ward, her hallucinations had apparently ceased, but psychotic ideas were very much in evidence. She appeared frightened and confused, but was well enough to be difficult with the ward personnel. Her disturbed ideas and their subsequent modification illustrate quite well the learning factors that are present in a psychotic episode.

When first seen, the patient immediately declared that she had now discovered the real reason for her breakdown. It had to do with the fact that at the age of seven or eight, she was raped in the garage of her home by a gardener. She screamed for help. Her mother came and watched the scene, giving the gardener certain suggestions as to how to proceed. In a subsequent interview, the patient declared that she had since spoken to her father about this incident in order to get more facts. He maintained that the gardener had attempted some kind of sex play with the child, but was caught before anything happened and fired.

A few days later, the patient produced another memory: At the age of thirteen, during one of her mother's numerous hospitalizations for a variety of psychosomatic illnesses, her father had her sleep in his bed and had put his arms about her. She also remembered, or thought she remembered, that on the following morning, her father fired the nurse who was taking care of her in her mother's absence for having criticized his intimacy with his daughter. The patient stressed the pathogenic nature of this incident during the next week or two, while the original story about the gardener began to fade out. At the same time she minimized the importance of similar incestuous material that she reported about incidents that had occurred only two months before her hospitalization.

For example, at home during the spring vacation, almost daily she would lie in bed between her parents, and, too, her father had a habit of entering her room at any time. She found these points unimportant in comparison to the incident at the age of thirteen.

Finally, during one of her first overnight leaves from the hospital, her father left the parental bedroom door ajar, and the patient coming to the door observed him naked in the adjoining bathroom. This incident, which appears to have been seized upon by the patient because on other occasions he had behaved in a similar manner, now enabled her to accuse her father openly of seductiveness. There was a very heated discussion when therapist and family met in the next treatment session, the parents jumping on their daughter for her constant interference with their privacy. Her mother made the statement: "Jane, you have always tried to interfere between me and your father for the past twenty years." Remember that, at the time, the patient was only nineteen.

All these incidents seem to be highlights in the evolution from psychotic fantasy to actual fact. To explain the steps of this development simply in relation to the patient's growing adaptation to reality does not seem to cover the essence of the phenomenon. Admittedly, more absurd formulations of the problem were gradually abandoned in favor of more realistic ones: for instance, the shift from the gardener's to father's behavior in the past, and from there to the present, as well as the shift from the actively abetting mother to the openly critical nurse and then to the passively resigned mother. But it seems that each phase contained its own *reductio ad absurdum*; in each instance, there was *one* element just a little "too good to be true," which then enabled and even compelled the patient to look around and explore further until reality eventually broke through in a veritable uproar during a joint family session.

At this point, the family therapist intervened with a forcefully framed instruction: the father was to abandon his passive, despairing attitude toward his wife and daughter and adopt the active role of referee between them. The patient became panicky and accused the therapist of betraying her and leaving her at the mercy of the person least suited for this role. By the following morning, however, she was calm and collected and began to realize that her father's role was precisely the one that would enable her to establish a more healthy relationship with him. Only a week later, she announced that she was now ready to return home, although until then she had refused to leave the hospital on the grounds that she could not live under the same roof with her father. She was discharged on the following day and has remained out of the hospital ever since.

Another change occurred during this patient's improvement, this time in relation to her mother. After her discharge from the hospital, much time and effort had to be spent in individual therapy as well as in family therapy working on the mother-daughter relationship. On the surface, the relationship was characterized by mutual tears, accusations, and attacks in anticipation of expected attacks, with the daughter caricaturing teen-age defiance and the mother helplessness and self-pity. Underneath the surface, and unrecognized, there was an almost continual interchange of double-level messages that kept mother and daughter locked in bitter, hopeless struggle. One afternoon they came to blows, and, after a brief fight, the mother managed to get a hold on the girl's wrists, immobilizing her, and repeating over and over again: "Go to your room, go to your room immediately." At this point, the patient was struck by the absurdity of the situation, and for the first time was able to comment on the inconsistency: "How can you expect me to go to my room if you're holding me here?"

Jane's earlier attempts to respond adequately to such contradictory behavior had, almost of necessity, been unsuccessful. In addition, she had found it impossible to cope with her father's seductiveness. Had she been able to say openly what she knew, she would not have got anywhere. In fact, she would only have reinforced her parents' united front against her. To complain about the incestuous situation and the damage she felt that it was doing to her personality development (especially to her relationship with her mother) was as impossible as to try to defend herself at the age of thirteen against father's advances in mother's absence. Her fear of attacking her father directly at this age was reinforced by the fate of the nurse who she believed was fired for criticizing him. At the age of nineteen, however, when her problems in relation to her father were revived by a serious romantic involvement with a young man, and when the label on her behavior had been changed from "wrong" or "bad" to "psychiatric illness," she could afford to bring about a repetition of the incident. It is as though she could then say to her father, "Now I have caught you. You are still doing it to me"—and in a situation that had the additional advantage of having mother present as a witness.

In this matter of labels lies one of the important differences between neuroses and schizophrenia. The neurotic can complain about some kind of pain or unhappiness, but the psychotic cannot. Because we have reason to think that, on the whole, the schizophrenic experiences terrible loneliness, self-doubt, and confusion, it may seem strange that he does not seek help long before social pressures bring him into the psychiatrist's office. The difference lies partially in the label attached to the two conditions. The neurotic and those around him recognize that something has occurred (stress or conflict, for example), whereas the schizophrenic is living in a situation that is constantly labeled normal by his family. This is nowhere more obvious than in initial interviews with the families of chronic schizophrenic patients wherein no one is unhappy about anything other than the fact that Jim or Mary happens to be "sick." It is a superhuman task for the patient to point out that this is not the only problem in the family. If this task is to be accomplished at all, it probably can be done only by crazy behavior.

It is difficult even for normal people to rely on their own perceptions and to defend them in the face of massive group disqualification. Take, for instance, the experiment in which a group is asked to guess the relative size of lines flashed on a screen. Unbeknown to the "victim," everyone else has been asked to falsify his actual impressions and strongly defend the false answers. The poor creature who has to doubt his own eyesight or go against the group is in a very difficult spot and often manifests seriously disturbed behavior.

The problem of making mistakes as a result of being told by a part of one's receptive faculties that one thing is true while another part contradicts it has appeared so often that the study of communication and its relation to mental disorders has become an area of specialization per se, one particularly important to any relationship between interaction and individual behavior. Witness my very real feelings about my pretended parents' comments on Korea or Jane's sudden realization that her mother was holding her wrists and ordering her to her own room. The first is a case of lack of verbal communication; the second combines words and actions. What does Jane's mother mean? What does she want? What is the appropriate response? A small child in a similar situation may be able to speak up as Jane did, but all too often he will not recognize the inconsistency as such, or, if he does, will not feel able to talk back to mother and tell her that, in the circumstances, she is asking the impossible. Extreme and necessary dependence, a very strong desire to do what she wants him to do in order to keep her love, a feeling of helplessness in the face of authority (or at least superior size)—these and many perfectly ordinary elements of any small child's life may very well keep him from coping with such a situation in any satisfactory way.

All human beings communicate in several ways—by word, tone, inflection, gesture, posture, facial expression, and so forth—and are quite capable of using more than one way at a time. Think, for example, about telephone behavior. You talk to a friend about picnic plans, smiling all the while, demonstrating the height of the sandwich pile with one hand and tapping your foot with impatience to be off. Your friend can't see, but you go right on using these natural forms of communication, anyway. Then you answer the phone to hear your boss asking that the special report be ready Monday instead of Wednesday. The picnic is off; your weekend is ruined. You scowl, glare out the window, clench the receiver, and slap the other hand angrily against your thigh, all the while saying in amiable tones, "Of course—no trouble at all—I'll be delighted—8:15 sure . . ." Your boss can't see you either, fortunately. Both friend and boss have to rely on words, tone of voice, inflections—verbal communication on the telephone.

Now consider a mother and her small child face to face. Mother is preoccupied because that morning father was anxious about a business conference, snapped at her, and generally made breakfast miserable for everyone. How is the meeting going? What will his mood be like at 5:30? Johnny gets the usual patient answers to his questions, but he senses, perhaps from the delay in response or the faraway look, that mother is only partly with him. He may respond by becoming anxious, too, getting fretful and cranky, or by going away to play by himself until mother is ready to behave "properly" and devote her full attention to him. He is responding not just to her spoken words, but also to her general attitude of the moment. This kind of two-message situation need not be particularly confusing, at least not more than momentarily, for Johnny knows that she isn't always this way, and he trusts that all will be well soon. Everyone must learn to deal with this situation sooner or later, and no harm done. It is certainly possible for human beings to receive more than one message at a time.

But suppose the messages are contradictory and yet demand a single response. Another mother stiffens, draws back, and frowns in disgust as she says, "Come here, Bobbie dear, and kiss me." Bobbie must do what she wants in order to please her and protect their relationship. Does she want what she says or what she does? He can't ask, perhaps because he has asked before and learned that she will vehemently deny any contradiction, thus confusing him more. (Jane was nineteen before she dared point out that she could not go to her room and remain within her mother's grasp.)

And suppose that Bobbie's father is reading the evening newspaper. If he speaks up and says, "Son, kiss your mother," Bobbie gets support for his feeling that he has received a kissing message. If father says (as is possible, but less usual in this culture), "Don't bother, son; she obviously doesn't mean it," then Bobbie's perception of rejection is backed up. (This second situation is far from ideal, but at least Bobbie knows where he stands.) But if father says nothing, the implication is that he supports both sides of mother's message, and Bobbie is left with a contradiction verified by both parents. This third situation we have called the double-bind.

In the early stages of our thinking, we tended to focus on the double-bind as it occurred between mother and child. But with more research, we have come to realize that the problem is much more complicated. True enough, the disturbed communication may first appear in specific words and actions of the mother-child pair, but further exploration almost always turns up another disturbed relationship—and all too often several others. For example, as Lidz suggested, mother might not have functioned this way had it not been for father's problems. So while the concept of the double-bind is still useful as a term descriptive of a certain type of behavior, it cannot be considered an isolatable single cause of mental disturbance. Furthermore, the bind may be exerted by father or by a brother or sister.

Because the family is a system, everyone's behavior influences and is influenced by everyone else's behavior. Beyond question, the children are as involved as the parents, and although the parents act as models for the child's behavior, the child's behavior continues to reinforce the parental behavior and thus makes change difficult. Suppose the parents have unconsciously taught a child to withdraw when they are unhappy in order not to be bothered by him. If their mood changes and they suddenly want a response, the child may at first withdraw in confusion. It is then easy for the parent to feel rebuffed and reject the child further. Where do genes come into all this? It is quite possible that some children inherently fit a family pattern because of their biological makeup. What behavior patterns may be linked to biological tendencies and how important such linkage is remain for science to work out. My impression, based on what is now known, is that the infant is so remarkably adaptable that only in rare cases does his biological response become crucial to his future mental health.

But perhaps at this juncture it would be useful to look at a disturbed family in action, so to speak. It can be, of course, only a small sample of the behavior of a single family group, but it should illuminate some of the theoretical remarks about communication and mental disturbance, in this case, schizophrenia. Remembering that there are virtually as many patterns as there are families, look for these generalized points in the following material. They are typical of the ways that the family of a schizophrenic operates.

First, family members typically qualify their own statements in an unclear, incongruent fashion. Most people do this at certain times—for example, when they are trying to tell the boss in a nice way that he is wrong. But in these families, the amount of incongruity seems rather large. If a family member says something critical of another family member, he will usually smile, thus disqualifying the criticism. Or he may indicate a criticism, but claim that it does not apply at this time. And so forth.

Second, the family members tend to disqualify one another's statements: that is, they neither confirm them nor disagree with them. It becomes difficult to know how one member is taking the remark of another member, because it is not labeled by the other member's actions as rude or improper or pleasant or whatever.

Three, family coalitions tend to be rare—except between parents against the mental disorder of the child. That is, if the mother claims that the patient is "talking crazy," the father will usually back her up. But such coalitions are not acknowledged by the members of this system, and, on other points, they agree not at all.

Four, characteristically, the mother is blameless and defends herself against any implication of blame by bringing in outside occurrences, acts of God, or misunderstandings on someone else's part. The father supports her in her blameless state either by not commenting, by being withdrawn and passive, or by constantly redefining every point so that "just what do you mean by that" is always the issue, and nothing can be taken personally or allowed to apply to his spouse.

This particular family consists of a mother, a father, a twenty-four-year-old daughter, who had been hospitalized for over five years for schizophrenia, and an older brother, who lives in another part of the country and almost never sees his family. The transcription comes from the first session that the therapist had with the father, the mother, and the daughter jointly.

MOTHER [to Father]: You talk.
FATHER: It's your show.
THERAPIST: No, it's all of yours.
M: It was very pleasant. We had a very nice weekend. Barbara wanted to see an art show, so I drove her into town Sunday morning, and we had a very pleasant weekend, didn't we Papa?
F: Yes, yes.
T [to Father]: Did you go along? [From Mother's behavior, Therapist senses Father was not present.]
F: No, I stayed home and worked Sunday morning, as usual.
T: Do you like to work around the place or on your office work?
F: Yes. [Evidently referring to "office work," but not saying so clearly.]
T [to Mother]: What seemed to be pleasant about it?
M: Barbara was her old self.
F: It was Barbara's proposal to go in and see the show. [Note the parental coalition, Father repeating what Mother has already said.]
M: Her proposal . . .
F: We were happy about that.
T: Well, does she have the responsibility of determining how things in the family go—happy or unhappy? Is she sort of your weather vane?
M [laughing]: Well, anyway, we're just fine when she is happy. Then everything is all right. [Note that this is a very indirect answer to Therapist's question. Barbara's happiness is mentioned, not the parents'; unhappiness is ignored.]

T: I was thinking of what a tough spot that is for her to be in. You know, the feeling "when I'm down, the rest of the family is down; then if I get up again, they'll come up with me." It's like walking around with a huge weight. Do you see that it might be difficult?

F: Well, it can't very well be any different. The girl has had a shock and naturally . . . [Evidently referring to her breakdown many years before, but again not making himself clear.]

M: I was just so glad that she wanted to go in, and I was tickled to death we saw the pictures and came back. It isn't always that way. We had quite a full life and so on. You see, she hasn't been at home for six years.

T: Well, what else? You went into the museum on Sunday morning.

M: Came back, had a late dinner, and Barbara looked at the TV, and then we all looked at it.

T: You watched . . .

M [interrupting him]: And while we slept, Barbara wrote a letter to her best girl friend while we took a nap because we had been out Saturday night, and Barbara very nicely wanted us to go, and we were out from eight-thirty to ten-thirty. [Note how all responses continue to be centered around the patient.]

T: Well, what did you do, where did you go?

F: Oh, just visited this friend's house and the friend's apartment. [Father gets away from daughter as topic.]

M: That was the first time we really left her and went out. She wanted us to and it went very nicely. [But Mother brings her back in.]

T: Well, that's fine. [to Patient] What did you do while they were gone? Watch TV or read or what?

PATIENT: I *think* I read. [Very quiet voice. Patient disqualifies own statement by tone and by "think." She has not spoken before.]

T [approvingly]: At least it wasn't so bad that you weren't able to concentrate while they were gone. [to parents] How long has it been since the two of you were out together, would you say? [Obviously means parents, but again . . .]

M: All *three* of us? [Patient is included.]

T: No, I mean just the two of you.

M: Well, since she's been home, I guess, isn't it?

F: Yes, one other time. [Supports Mother with "yes," and then corrects her.]

M: Oh, yes, we did. Saturday afternoon, a cocktail party. We had my cleaning woman in. She is a very nice woman who just loves young people and children. She offered to come any time she could and the first time she came she stayed for two hours. But this is the first time in a long time that Barbara stayed alone.

T: Well, that might encourage you to do it more often, do you think? Is that all right with you, Barbara?

F: Yes, she's been very good about letting us go out. [What is the meaning of this remark when (1) Patient is not allowed to speak for herself and (2) parents have left her alone only *one* time?]

M: Oh, yes.

F: She's very cooperative.

T [to Father]: I imagine in some ways you might feel a little roped into this interview. I am aware that your wife can be pretty persuasive. [Mother laughs.]

T [still addressing Father]: As I told your wife, it was more or less up to me over a period of time to see if I could sell you on the notion that there was something here for you. Otherwise, if you just come along, it's simply another body in the room and won't amount to much. In order to help me get some picture, is there anything currently about your *own* situation you would like to change? In terms of your responses to other people?

F: The problem is simply to help Barbara get adjusted to the way of life, and I think we're making reasonable progress. I think it's going to work itself out all right so I'm not going around under the burden of a terrific problem. Of course, we are facing—getting along all right. [Shuts off any implication of personal needs and leaves responsibility with Patient.]

T: Apart from Barbara's difficulties, everything would be just fine?

F: Yes, I think so. Just the usual problems, and it doesn't pay to worry about those.

M: Yes, that's our major problem.

F: It's just a period of readjustment. [Note strong parental agreement that Barbara is the only problem.]

T [to Mother]: What would you say about that?

M: I agree with him one hundred percent, because they are both the same kind of people [looking at her daughter]—enjoying the same kind of things, and if she could just get well and ask for records occasionally to be played and to play the piano together occasionally [that is, she and Father], well, I agree one hundred percent. [What is meant by the statement that Father and daughter are the same kind of people? Is Father a problem to her, too?]

T: Now I'm not sure that you *are* agreeing with him. Let me see, you lost me. Your husband was saying there was nothing about himself or his way of life—that everything would be fine if Barbara's problem would be solved.

M: Her being sick. There would be no problem at all if she were well.

F: Sure, we are in agreement on that. [Again strong support and parental coalition.]

T: Do you feel that if Barbara were well and living somewhere else things would be better for you?

M: No, not necessarily. If she wants to, okay, but right there with us is perfectly okay. We like the same kind of things, the same kind of people. There isn't any problem. [Is Mother referring to daughter or to Father?]

F: Let's not make problems where none exist.

T: Believe me, I don't want to do that, either. On the other hand, I don't want to overlook any that do exist. Otherwise, I wouldn't be of much use to you. You see, it's a little puzzling to me how Barbara would get sick in the first place if there wasn't something wrong, except for her being sick. I don't quite understand it.

M: Oh, well, perhaps you won't understand the gravity of what she's been through and that she has been sick before this, and so on. I feel sure, at least, I hope, that when things get settled down. . . . Now yesterday she had a bad day because she tried to write to her girl friend. She thought that when she had written Sunday, while we were asleep, she had said too much, had asked too many favors. So she struggled all morning trying to do this letter, and I went out and left her alone. She got rapidly worse until I sort of persuaded her to stop and rest and then it got too late, about five o'clock, for the mail and so I said it didn't have to be written, anyway. I didn't say that in the beginning because she really wanted to write it. I let her go along, but when I let her write, a whole sort of crisis developed about it. I . . .

T: I don't want to go off on a tangent, but I wonder if this happens very often. That is, I would say there seems to be something in the family situation that contributes to this difficulty.

M: Okay, that's why a doctor has to help me. Maybe I did wrong to let her write the letter; then probably the day would have been different. After all, I want a doctor to help me. I try my best, but I just play by ear, sometimes it works and sometimes it doesn't, that's why I want you to help me, not to play by ear. [With increasing irritation.]

But tell me what I should have done and point out what I should do. Should I have let her gone ahead and write the letter? What would you have done? Everything I've done ever since she was born, I've tried to do my best. I'm willing to do everything for her. If she likes to sleep, I let her. What would you have done? We had a bad day yesterday, not nearly as bad as two other days we had, but it was sort of bad. We got the letter yesterday about the settlement [for an accident]. She told you she was willing to sign it. Now it would be a very nice thing if she could sign that today, and we could get it in the mail. [Brings letter and form out of her purse.] It is to get it signed so we can get the money. I haven't told Barbara the letter just came last night at six o'clock, and that was no time to tell her on a bad day. Now if she signs this, and we send it right back, then the whole thing will be taken care of. [Note that Mother brings along the letter and form, which the patient has not seen, so the Therapist can help her.]

You will observe several things about this excerpt. One is the mother's tremendous devotion to her daughter. Notice that as soon as the therapist mentioned that the patient might get well and live somewhere else, the mother, in a somewhat anxious tone, stated that it was all right for her to live with her parents. The father's reply was very obscure: "Let's not make problems where none exist." What does this mean? Because it is said to the therapist, presumably he means, "Don't try to cause trouble by intervening between my wife and daughter. I have learned not to do this myself."

Note also that the parents agree on the topic of their daughter's condition as their major problem. This is the only thing they are able to agree on, and even here they don't agree completely, because there are implications about who is more at fault, how "sick" she is, and the nature of her disorder. The father espouses a more strictly organic cause, whereas the mother feels that the fact that they were away from her so much when she was a child may have played a part.

Notice also that at the end of the excerpt, the mother produces a form that she wants Barbara to sign. This is typical of the behavior that caused the patient's mistrust of her parents in the first place, as was proved in later interviews. At this point, the therapist took the position that he did not know the family well enough to suggest whether Barbara should sign or not, and that he did not want to take sides. Naturally, the mother denied that there were any sides. The therapist suggested to Barbara that she take the letter home, read it, think about it, and then decide whether she wanted to sign. This episode had a surprising outcome. The patient decided to visit the lawyer herself, even though it meant a trip of several hours, and her mother became upset, declaring that Barbara couldn't manage it. Supported by the therapist, the patient handled her mother very creditably, and later made the trip successfully.

Another session with this family involved the patient's brother. Until recently, the general feeling has been that the siblings of schizophrenics did quite well. (This, as we have seen, helped establish the idea that schizophrenia is a recessive hereditary disorder.) My own experience has been quite different, and it is supported by a few recent reports. In general, earlier sibling studies consisted only of interviewing one of the schizophrenic's brothers or sisters for an hour or two, and never seeing them in the family context. For example, if one had seen Barbara's brother in a single interview and by himself, he would have been impressed by a personable, articulate, young man who was sorry for his sister's difficulties, but couldn't have felt more unlike her. On the other hand, seeing him with the rest of the family during several interviews revealed quite another picture. Although when he was absent from our meetings, he was described by his parents as a paragon of all the virtues, their attitude was quite different in their personal contacts.

Initially, in the family sessions, the brother denied having much recollection of his sister, as he had left home at a rather early age to go to school. Let us pick up an interview at a point at which the therapist asked him directly to recall something about his early experiences with her.

SON: We used to fight a lot. Until, let's see what age, maybe as late as twelve.

T: When you were twelve, you mean?

S: Yes, maybe not quite that late. Around there, I'm not sure.

T: What kind of thing would you fight about?

S: Probably I was just teasing her. As I recall, I wasn't mature enough to fight about anything specifically. Well, for something to do. Bored.

T [to Father]: Do you remember the fighting? What is your impression of what it was about? Did you feel it was a teasing sort of thing?

S [cutting in]: On my part I don't think there was any animosity. It was a pretty superficial thing, as far as I remember. [Father remains silent.]

T [to Mother]: Do you remember the fighting?

M: Well, all I remember is that on the back seat they used to kick each other's shin sometimes. We didn't have a car until the war because we were always living in the city and didn't need one. And then suddenly, in 1940, I guess it was 1939, we got the car, so that made you how old when we had it?

S: About nine. 1939, so that makes nine.

M: That was something. I don't ever remember fighting on

the boat. You were a bit older then. Couple of years older. [Notice the quick switch to the boat where they didn't fight.]

S: You got rid of it in 1941. It was around then.

M: He [Father] didn't have any interest in boats. He wouldn't have anything to do with it or work on it or do anything with it. I don't think either of them were very interested in the boat. We couldn't go to Europe, and I happened just that time to get some extra money. We bought a boat, and as I was raised on the water and used to boats and . . .

T: Was it some kind of a sailboat?

F: A 32-foot cruiser.

M: And as I talked him into it, then he went all overboard for boats much more than I did. I was so tired of it. It was so much work to keep up, and neither of us had time to do it, and I told him, and he still likes boats, and I can't bear the sight of them, but neither of the children took much to the boat . . . [How does one account for the switch from the previous statement, "He wouldn't have anything to do with it"?]

T: Quite a bit of boat.

S: Yup, 32-foot.

T: Where did you cruise?

S: On Lake Michigan right across the canal, and on the Mississippi River, and St. Paul one summer when we were staying on a farm there.

M: We took them from the Mississippi down.

T [to Patient]: Well, was this the summer that you were in that camp you've spoken of? [The Patient had indicated timidly in previous sessions that she was shipped off to schools and camps a good deal.]

M [cutting in]: Yes, Minnesota. And Barbara came home

feeling pretty low . . . [Note that Mother answers for daughter.]

S [cutting in]: It was during the war and . . .

M: Minnesota it was. They were staying in Minnesota. So this summer we went up and brought them back in the sailboat.

T: Well, you had the cruiser too?

S: Yeah.

T: You had the sailboat at the time, though?

M: No.

S: Also the cruiser.

M: Of course. We didn't go out all the time but we had fun.

T: You had the cruiser before . . .

F: Sold the cruiser.

M: That's right, the sailboat.

S: Didn't get the cruiser either until we came back from Europe in 1939 or 1940.

M: 1940. But we couldn't take it through the locks so it had to be the cruiser. [Does some of this confusion result from being uncomfortable about the subject of camps and Barbara's feeling low and trying to avoid it?]

S: Well, now [tentatively], every summer we were in a sort of camp-farm or farm-camp something like that.

M: It's always that he's wanted to go. [Firmly looking at her son.]

S: Well, yeah, as she got older. [Looking at sister.]

T: Whatever that means. [Puzzled at switch in topic.]

M: Well, then she didn't go. Well, then she didn't go because he continued to go, and she didn't. Well, kid stuff. I hate to talk about this.

S: Well, as I remember, all through this I don't think Barbara played a very big part in my life, well not a conscious part, because I really have difficulty in recalling her, how she acted and how she felt, and so on to the age of twelve or so.

T: You might have been a little less close than some brothers and sisters are?

S: Perhaps.

M [defensively]: Age difference was about three years and three months.

S: Well, as I recall, I don't think she was particularly happy in this period. When we were always together up until eleven or twelve. These summer camp sessions and other times.

T: And she would not be apt to let you know that she was pretty unhappy. So I wonder what clues you picked up to tell how she felt?

S: Well, we were usually at different camps . . . it's hard to remember. [But he has just said "we were always together."]

Finally the parents spoke up about how much of the time the children were left in camps, and the brother agreed tentatively. He was punished for this by mother's bringing up some of his "wild" behavior, and the topic drifted away from camps. You notice how confused the discussion is. Yet, at several points, the mother speaks up loud and clear, particularly when the brother states that every summer he and his sister were in some sort of camp, and his mother announces that he had wanted to be. Again, when he switches to his sister from himself, his mother makes clear that this is a forbidden topic, and he complies by saying that he doesn't recall much about his sister.

Despite his taking an in-between position, the brother's visits were very helpful. His behavior and recollections exploded the myth that he and his sister were totally different, he the paragon, she the problem, especially when he discussed his unhappy late adolescence. He even stated: "I haven't been around much since thirteen or so, going away to school and all—that may have helped." There seems to be some awareness of the possible dangers of staying within the family circle.

One of the most rewarding occurrences in family therapy is the discovery of a piece of family interaction or behavior that explains one of the patient's symptoms. In this sense, schizophrenia and schizophrenic symptoms are adaptive behavior. For example, Barbara's parents complained more about her indecisiveness than about anything else. Evidently, it was a problem when she got up in the morning and thought about what to wear, and everything else in the day produced a similar crisis. But in all the family's conversation it is strikingly apparent that whenever Barbara makes a decision, the parents refute it in some way, and then she backs out—unless she has support from outside the family group. Yet her parents do not and cannot see themselves as having anything to do with her indecision.

These parents and others like them are not deceitful or mean; they simply act out a pattern in which they and the patient are hopelessly caught. Part of this pattern consists of their having contradictory expectations of the child and being unaware that they do. In time, the child (in this case Barbara) can no longer say, "Look here, I can't do X *and* Y. Make up your minds."

The parents of schizophrenics have been found to have contradictory expectations of the child who became schizophrenic as compared to his brothers and sisters. Expectations of dependence and responsibility were measured by a sociologist, who at the same time was impressed by the fact that although the preschizophrenic and his nonschizophrenic siblings were reared in the same family, they were not exposed to the same social and psychological conditions in different periods of their lives. This variation may start even before birth or be evident during infancy. The special circumstances surrounding the preschizophrenic's birth or infancy define the special role that he will later occupy in the total family constellation, as well as the special role that he is to play in relation to his parents. In addition, the fact that the child who later becomes a schizophrenic plays such a role may assist his siblings in not having to accept a similar fate, but the disturbed child continues to fit into the situation by persistent efforts to fulfill contradictory expectations and thus reinforces the parents' pattern.

In Barbara's family, these contradictions were very evident. For example, both the mother and the father wished to pursue careers and therefore did not welcome the early pregnancy. On the other hand, they both had high goals for their daughter. As a result Barbara was supposed to keep out of the way and not interfere with her parents' lives and at the same time attain goals that could be reached only with parental interest and stimulation.

Perhaps many of you will have read the excerpt about Barbara and asked yourselves, "So what? This doesn't sound to me much different from what goes on in many families that don't have schizophrenics." Such skepticism is well founded at present. The study of the family is a recondite matter, and researchers have only recently begun to explore the field. In Chapter 9 we shall see what they are doing.

But meanwhile, as a treatment method, the analysis and modification of such family behavior produces results. It seems quite possible, therefore, that lurking in this material lies information about cause as well as treatment of mental disorder, even though we have not yet isolated any single factor. But then, neither have the geneticists or the biochemists.

CHAPTER 9

STUDYING THE FAMILY

NOT TOO MANY years ago, the newspapers carried photographs of appealing, big-eyed, baby monkeys clinging to large, big-eyed, terrycloth-and-wire figures. These were "substitute mothers," shaggy, warm, and always available, and for some time the babies seemed to be doing fairly well. But, first, it was found that when they were brought up by such a mother in an individual cage and without other baby monkeys around, they never did come to get along with the group as well as other monkeys. This discovery and the passing of time led to the study of adult monkeys, twenty females and twenty males, who had been so raised. Then, second, it was found that the males showed no normal or adequate sexual behavior, and the females not only failed to show normal sexual behavior, but when they did bear children, tended to ignore them or attack them. Thus, the old idea of "maternal instinct" has been put into question.

If monkeys don't have it, what of the more advanced human being? Monkeys are important in such research because they have close kinship bonds with man in terms of their relatively long developmental period, which necessitates close ties between mother and infant, and because they subsequently enter stages of social interaction with other monkeys that have definite human analogies. These later similarities were attested by the curator of the Sarawak Museum in Kuching, Sumatra. He and his wife tried to rear orangutans so that they could later be returned to the jungle, but they failed. The animals develop so slowly that they adopt human attitudes, and will not leave for the jungle. Only the zoo and its human contacts will do. "After being raised in a home and getting a proper upbringing, they become spoiled and aren't fit for jungle life."

By this time, the importance of environment during the early years is quite generally accepted. Women's magazines and the Sunday supplements of newspapers regularly add to the voluminous writing on the topic. Not only animal experiments but studies of human infants continue to prove the point, and although mother remains the most important figure, more and more attention is being given to father's influence, with the result that nurturing research is becoming family research.

But in spite of the widespread dissemination of such findings when they are applicable to the so-called normal, relatively healthy family, less—in fact, little—is reported in the news media about research on early environment and its connection with mental disorder.

Troubled children come from troubled homes—a widely recognized generalization certainly, but much more needs to be said. An overall picture of distress: One hundred psychopathic children (64 severely enough disturbed to be sent to a mental hospital for observation as psychopathic delinquents) had family and social backgrounds that were far from ordinary. The children usually came from disrupted families. In only 20 cases was the father or his substitute in a stable job. Alcoholism and physical violence were common in the homes; and in 11 cases, one of the parents had been in jail. In some families, the girls had been subjected to rape and incest. Of course, heredity might be responsible for such parental behavior, although only the "bad blood" or "poor stock" theories, unsupported by scientific evidence, as we have seen, would account for it.

Furthermore, the broken home, so often mentioned in connection with emotional disturbance, produces information relevant to the point. Two thousand families of University of California students showed that if neither set of a student's grandparents had divorced, only 15 percent of their children's marriages broke up. But if one pair of grandparents divorced, 25 percent of their children did. If both sets of grandparents were divorced, 40 percent of their children's marriages also ended in the divorce courts. These figures contrast with those from the University of Notre Dame (largely Catholic); less than 5 percent of the graduates over the past fifty years have been divorced. Heredity?

The state of California has a divorce rate double the national average, 50 marriages out of every 100 ending in the divorce court. In San Francisco, the figure rises to 55 of 100. The remarriage rate is tremendous among individuals in their twenties and thirties, and often the remarriage takes place after a very brief courtship; the divorce rate in second marriages continues to be high. Neither psychiatry nor sociology knows why this should be so in California, and especially in San Francisco, but it would seem presumptuous to blame heredity. Perhaps the divorce rate is linked with whatever factors give San Francisco one of the highest suicide rates in the nation, but on the evidence of eminent medical geneticists, suicidal tendencies are not hereditary.

Information more specific and directly related to mental disorder concerns the loss of a parent during early childhood, not by divorce or separation, but by death. For example, more mothers of almost a thousand neurotic patients had died before the child was nine than had the mothers of the population as a whole. And three times as many hospitalized psychotic patients had so lost their mothers as had the average child. The impact of maternal death seems to be more serious for girls, who are most vulnerable before the age of three, than for boys, but this effect may not become obvious until adulthood. The death of a father apparently does not have the same force. When it occurs before the child is five, it is not apparently related to later neurosis. But there is evidence to suggest that the loss of a father may play a role in subsequent delinquency in boys and in some males who later become schizophrenic.

Among depressed patients, childhood bereavement is more common than among the general population. Forty-one percent of an English group, for example, were orphaned before they were fifteen years old. More than the average number had lost one or another parent before fourteen, and a high proportion had no knowledge at all of one or the other parent. Generally speaking, the most common situations precipitating depressive illness in adults are broken love affairs, loneliness, marital difficulties, death of a spouse or relative, loss of a job, trivial quarrels, and very occasionally such physical factors as influenza and surgery. All these situations involve some degree of loss or a feeling of rejection (which means emotional loss), so the statistics come as no surprise to the practicing therapist.

Obviously, the influence of the death of a parent on the emotional development of a child depends on earlier relationships within the home as well as the maintenance of the home afterward. A variety of protective factors can help the individual deal with this traumatic event—obviously, because the majority of those who have lost a mother in early childhood have escaped serious emotional illness. When compatible relationships had existed in the childhood home, when each parent had had a well-defined role, and when the home was kept intact after the loss of the parent, it has been demonstrated that the child can grow into a reasonably well-adjusted adult. Protection against the shock of parental loss can also be supplied by sources outside the home—other relatives, church, community—and, when the father has died, by the mother's ability to accept such support without feeling humiliated. The threat to the family is greater when the mother has died, because the father is less likely to keep the children with him, usually for economic reasons.

When a parent has been lost through suicide, the traumatic effect of the parent's having taken his own life, added to the emotional climate and the events preceding such a step, usually produces maladjustment in the child's later life. Many cases record the suicide of an adult at about the same age that his parent had committed suicide.

Closely allied is "the anniversary hypothesis," a phenomenon described by Josephine Hilgard and her associates. A group of patients have been found to have their first psychotic episodes when their (usually oldest) children are very nearly the age that they were when they lost a parent. Each one becomes a patient, it would seem, in order to reenact a significant event in his own childhood—an anniversary of trauma that results not from his own age now but from the age of his child now, which corresponds to his age at the time of his parent's death.

One such case involves Mrs. W., who, when she was nine years old, lost her mother by death. Mrs. W. entered a mental hospital for the first time, depressed and having made a suicide attempt, when her youngest daughter was eight. Her mother had had a stroke at Mrs. W.'s birth, and so she had been cared for by relatives during her first two years. Then, when she got home, she clung to her mother for the few years that remained before the older woman died. But there was evidence of guilty feelings about her mother's death because she was the child who had "caused" her mother's stroke.

For a number of years, Mrs. W. was apparently all right; she married and had two girls older than the daughter whose "anniversary" she celebrated by her suicide attempt. Her marriage was an unhappy one, but it managed to survive without any special crises. Of special interest are relatives' reports that this youngest girl reminded them of the patient when she was a little girl.

As Mrs. W. became more disturbed and depressed, she experienced many of the symptoms that her mother had had in the year before she died of her second stroke—headaches and dizzy spells like her mother's and a fear that she might suddenly drop dead. Although the patient had married and had children, the psychiatrists working with her found that in many ways she had remained a child, and tended to feel more in common with her children, particularly the youngest girl who resembled her, than with adults. The youngest daughter served as a constant reminder of the trauma that Mrs. W. had suffered when her own mother had died. Thus the early shock, the insecure feeling of living with various relatives, and the slight opportunity for real identification with her own mother—the woman who would ordinarily have provided the adult model for the little girl to identify with—all contributed to the background of her psychosis.

It should be pointed out, without going into technical and not very lively details, that these studies by Hilgard and her co-workers were very carefully done. Meticulous statistical analyses of the data and an adequate control group ensured that findings were not merely the result of chance. As a consequence, they discovered, for example, that anniversary psychoses were more common among psychotic female patients than among males, although as yet there is no explanation for this difference. But, at the same time, their data showed that a disproportionately large number of alcoholic, but not psychotic, men had lost a parent. Not having done the same amount of careful research on this particular problem, they draw no final conclusions, but they do feel that more is involved than statistical coincidence.

For example, Mr. X. was fifth of five children. When he was six years old, his parents separated, and when he was twelve his father died. Mr. X. married, had five children, and named the last child for himself. When this child was six, the patient left his family, and when the child was twelve, the patient was hospitalized for his alcoholic condition. One of his comments was that he never really knew why he had left his family six years before. Alcoholism seems to have substituted for psychosis in this and other cases, but the anniversary hypothesis remains a phenomenon in common. Unless death, psychosis, and alcoholism could be equated (but clearly they cannot be), and unless these patients were themselves the same age as their dying parents (but they are not, and *their* children's age is the critical factor), genes can have little to do with the regularity of these patterns. Family background and experience, yes, but not inherited characteristics.

Although it is not difficult to see how a family broken by divorce or death might prove extremely upsetting to a child, it is sometimes more difficult to find the reasons for disturbance. More and more studies are being done, however, on many phases of the situation, and gradually we are developing a body of information about the complexities of family interaction and the habitual patterns that can be set up for good or ill.

Let us take as an example a single family characteristic—obesity—and look at a few of its ramifications. Here the authority is Jean Mayer, of the Harvard School of Public Health, who has devoted a lifetime to the study of obesity and all its possible causes, endocrine, genetic, psychogenic, and metabolic. His genetic studies reveal that obese children are found in only 7 percent of families in which both parents are of normal weight; if one parent is obese, so are 40 percent of the children; and when both parents are obese, 80 percent are also. These figures suggest hereditary causation; when Mayer studied adopted children, however, they showed very similar percentages in relation to their adoptive parents' weight. As a result, the purely genetic hypothesis loses some of its strength, and family eating habits gain importance. In addition, obesity (and similar physical disorders) illustrates the complexities of heredity and environment and the ease with which the time factor or negative selection may be overlooked. For example, the obese child spends almost three times as many hours watching television as the average child and four times as much talking on the telephone. He chews 27 percent more gum. Classes of college freshmen show that the proportion of obese girls applying for higher education is far below the proportion in the population, although studies in high schools have shown that there is no difference between the scholastic ability of obese children and those of average weight.

It seems obvious when one puts these facts together that the obese child is discriminated against by his environment, and reacts by withdrawing either because of the actual discrimination or because of his fear that he will be discriminated against. The more time he spends by himself watching television, the more time and tendency he will have to become obese. The less exercise he gets, the more obese he becomes, and the greater the possibility that he will not try to exercise because of discrimination and ridicule when he tries to enter athletic competition or the like.

So too, if eating patterns in the home influence the child's weight, his tie to his home becomes stronger as he becomes heavier; the amount of time he spends at home increases; and hence his tendency to become obese is encouraged. The curious statistics about the admission of obese young women to colleges may indicate a negative-selective factor (in effect, a kind of prejudice) on the part of the educators, or it may indicate that these girls do not want to expose themselves to the atmosphere of the college campus where dating is all-important. Obviously, both these factors could be at work simultaneously. Then the girl who does not go away to college probably stays at home, and, if she belongs to a middle-class family, does not marry for some years—giving her more years around the house to increase her weight and hence the statistics.

That weight reduction can be accurately predicted has been known for over twenty-five years, but the obese patients are put to bed, and their diets and activities carefully supervised to make sure they can sneak no extras. Environment is forced upon them, so to speak, and inherited factors are apparently negligible. But if there is a genetic factor in obesity, it has the same import that we are postulating for heredity in relation to the ordinary mental disorders: the environment must participate with the genetic disability (if any) and, furthermore, the genetic disability will not keep environmental measures from being curative.

Obesity has another interesting aspect—the profound mental changes that sometimes follow precipitous loss of weight on a "crash" diet. The individual who is used to himself as fat and whose image of his body in some ways protects his image of his total self can undergo serious psychological changes when suddenly he has to accept a new appearance. These cannot be shown to be chemical changes (and furthermore they occur in other situations, as when some women who have had plastic surgery to correct flat chests undergo psychotic episodes). Much remains to be learned about the impressive influence of environmental change on the human biological condition, but clearly such influence exists.

On the other hand, the approach to biological changes in the mentally disturbed human has all too often been from the position that the change is a cause rather than an effect. Actually, there is no reason to believe that early maladaptation would not produce biological effects. Consistent exposure to frustration, rigid thinking patterns, and the like could very well set up patterns within the organism virtually unalterable at a later age. If this early patterning is reinforced over the years—and the family of childhood and adolescence tends to be much the same as the family of infancy—it is quite possible to see how an individual could be altered in a marked manner and eventually become unresponsive to change. When such a person is studied by a psychiatrist—or anyone—he may be considered to be "organically altered" (that is, truly changed in physical structure of some sort). Then the early and continuing pressures on him can be unrecognized or glossed over without difficulty.

Let me illustrate this point by giving you the highlights of the case of a young man who was hospitalized for schizophrenia at the age of nineteen. Both parents were ambitious professional people, shocked by the discovery of pregnancy soon after their marriage, and upset by the arrival of the infant and its effect on their professional plans, which had included extensive traveling. Although the delivery was ordinary enough, the mother was fearful lest the baby had been damaged in some way. She picked Ted up whenever he cried and sometimes spent most of the night rocking him. The father kept out of the way except when he reminded his wife that the baby's crying disturbed him and kept him from much-needed sleep.

Finally, a pediatrician prevailed on the mother to get a nurse, recognizing that the mother's fear and tension made the infant tense and hence started the crying cycle all over again. Although there was immediate improvement after the nurse arrived, the mother unfortunately felt that the new state of affairs reflected on her own adequacy, and she had her husband discharge the nurse after two weeks.

The mother's mother then moved in with the young couple and insisted that a strict schedule be maintained, even if it meant awakening the infant for feedings. Mother took to the schedule with great enthusiasm, and father, feeling even more left out and ignored, soon disappeared on a six-month business trip.

When Ted was a year old, his mother felt that she could resume her former activities, especially her trips with her husband and the freedom they meant. Until he was ten, the boy had a succession of nursemaids, his grandmother off and on, and an extremely tense, guilty, and doting mother when she was available. There was very little relationship between father and son in this period because father was extremely busy, and closeted himself in his study during the little time he was home. The boy, already shy and insecure, devoted himself to lonely pursuits, particularly reading (his mother's hobby) and listening to music (his father's).

When Ted was eleven, his father took a new job, partly at mother's insistence that the three must have more home life. This change was a mixed blessing, because now Ted had to bear the burden of guilt for making his parents move and his father change his job; in covert ways, it was constantly thrown up to him that he should be grateful for the sacrifices. In the new setting, it became more apparent to the boy that his parents got along very poorly with each other. He began to feel some responsibility for this condition, and tried to play the mediator's role. (It is interesting that years later, after he became psychotic, he often attacked both parents verbally for the way they treated each other.) The parents, without meaning to, misrepresented themselves to him, presenting a picture of successful, outgoing people who coped adequately with the outside world. Actually, both were tense, insecure, and of very little support to each other. In the main, each was comfortable only when alone, either reading or listening to music. But the impression of strength that the child overtly received increased his own sense of basic unworthiness in a world that was quite frightening and strange.

He managed to get through high school with fair success and was enrolled in a college selected as "the place to go" during his early childhood. In the first few months of his first semester, he first began to feel extraordinarily insecure, and then developed delusions of persecution, which led to his being hospitalized.

Ted was now officially labeled a mental patient, and for the next five years, in a series of mental hospitals, he underwent various kinds of psychiatric therapy, including shock treatments and individual psychotherapy. From time to time, he would improve enough to return home, but invariably he would be back in the hospital after a relatively short period.

His parents are sincerely convinced that Ted's emotional disorder was chemically caused. As evidence of an organic intractable disorder, they point to his frequent rehospitalizations. Other factors are ignored. Ted is overweight and socially shy. He has no vocation or training, and he came from a family in which one did not become a day laborer. The hospital developed into a haven, whereas home meant discomfort, embarrassment, and pressure to be like others his age who had long since passed him by. Furthermore, as the years slip past, the parents crystallize their picture of the patient, and more and more they see no connection between Ted and themselves. Once they might have recognized some of the intrafamily tensions, but now time has produced a mental block to such possibilities. Ted is "organically altered"—in their minds and his. And as a result, very little can be done for him. Genes, chemistry, or whatever, such a negative position is unsupported by the results produced in a more optimistic climate that recognizes the influences of environment and the possibilities of modifying it.

In Chapter 8, we saw the disturbed forms of communication that could make so large a difference in behavior—ordinary, neurotic, or psychotic. They likewise can create situations in which the family leaves the patient, perhaps verbally rather than physically, but nonetheless forcefully. One therapist tells the story of parents who for months had begged their hospitalized schizophrenic daughter to come home for a weekend. Then one day she asked whether she could make the visit soon. Father and mother continued their conversation as if nothing had been said until the therapist broke in, unbelieving, to ask whether they had not heard. The daughter asked again.

Apparently delighted, her parents asked formal permission, and then for twenty minutes they debated the arrangements for driving the girl to and from the house, both having cars and available time. Their daughter spent the weekend in the hospital, and, like Ted, she will no doubt continue to do so. The hospital provides her only available protection against such conflicting statements and the real rejection inherent in their leaving her there.

This girl's therapist is convinced that the schizophrenic "learns" his psychosis, the form of its symptoms (for example, withdrawal), their content (for example, paranoid delusions), and their uses (for example, to hold off the "real" world). And this learning is done at home, among the rest of the family.

Psychological testing as well as therapists' experiences point up the differences between families, and trained investigators can make distinctions with no other information before them than the test results. For example, Rorschach and Thematic Apperception Tests accurately sorted out families with schizophrenic children. Parents in these families fell into two groups, one blurring the entire situation from beginning to end, the second perceiving it accurately, but adding a twist of their own at the last minute. The experimenter's analogy is apt and interesting: The first group of families go to the zoo and argue about whether a certain animal is an elephant or a donkey and, in addition and virtually simultaneously, whether snakes have legs. The second all agree about the elephant with the trunk and the donkey with long ears, but just as their small child is getting the two clear in his mind, these parents tell him that the animals are really symbols of political parties, thus confusing him again and blurring the experience. Not surprisingly, the children in the first group are more disturbed; those in the second are borderline cases.

Elephants are real and so are donkeys. To the ordinary person they are not difficult to distinguish, but when there is constant confusion about them, their reality—not just the difference—is always in doubt. Suppose, however, that mother, for some reason of her own, firmly insisted that the one with the trunk was the donkey. Perhaps not until he was six and went to school would Billy have a chance to learn the generally accepted truth. And suppose the unreality of mother's statements is not so easily checked, as for example in the realm of ideas and abstractions. Because of her superior position in the early years, she can impose her own confused thinking on her children and involve them in her own particular unrealistic world. A patient who had been schizophrenic for many years once said, "I could have easily lived in the world had it turned out to be as Mother represented it to me. But growing up I realized the world was different. And I broke."

Emotional climate as well as the learning process is receiving more and more scientific attention. The two are closely related, of course, and experimenter and therapist alike agree that in most instances the difference is one of emphasis. We have already seen in Chapter 3 the beginnings of difference in environment, even for identical twins, within the uterus. Recently the emotional climate of the fetus, twin or not, has provided data not yet conclusive, but certainly suggestive. For example, L. W. Sontag has been involved with 300 children, beginning three or four months before birth. Information on fetal nutrition, activity, heart rate, and the like are collected at regular intervals, as are various maternal records. Among the 300, there have been five whose mothers have undergone strong emotional crises during pregnancy—for example, death of husband in the seventh month or abandonment by husband in the eighth month. When the physiological records of the fetus before and after the crisis are compared, they show that activity is increased four or five times (and in one case ten times), the fetal heart rate increased by twenty or twenty-five beats a minute, and these changes continued for several weeks. Although Sontag is well aware that his sample is very small and as yet statistically insignificant, he points out that all five were hyperactive babies. Furthermore, they had more bowel movements and more spitting up than the other babies, as well as tending to be irritable and restless.

Less melodramatic than father's death or disappearance, but also significant, are certain maternal attitudes and emotions. Women at a prenatal clinic during their last four weeks of pregnancy have been questioned about fears of harming the baby and feelings about pregnancy, and their answers compared with their babies' behavior in the hospital nursery during their first five days. A further set of questions dealt with age, education, order in the family, parents' education, number of marriages, number and age of other children, age of husband, belief in "planned pregnancy," planning for this pregnancy, and attitudes toward breast and bottle feeding. The babies' behavior was "scored" in terms of amount of crying, amount of sleep, degree of irritability, bowel movements, and feeding. Twenty-eight out of 163 had two or more days during which they showed unusual behavior, but there was no relationship between this behavior and any such factor as race, age of mother, length of labor, anesthesia, delivery, feeding, and planned pregnancy. (Although statistically insignificant in this particular study, it is amusing to note—and fortunate for the babies—that 67 percent of the mothers believed in "planned" pregnancy but only 32 percent had planned this one.)

What did prove important was the mother's fear of harming the unborn baby. The greater the fear, the greater the baby's disturbance. Nor did this depend on the mother's brief contacts (ten hours in five days) with the baby, because, for example, the one unwed mother, whose baby was to be adopted and who never saw him, was extremely fearful, and her baby was in the group whose behavior was classified as unusual.

Of course, in presenting these findings, no one means to imply that these babies will of necessity grow up to belong to the population of the mentally disturbed. But the earlier idea that babies are born with inherited constitutions may ignore important prenatal influences of psychological rather than genetic origin.

It is very difficult to find children born to two definitely schizophrenic parents, but eight have been located. Neatly (and coincidentally), four went to foster homes, and four stayed with their parents. Over their first year and a half, the foster children showed no signs of abnormal behavior. Neither did one of the "schizophrenic" group, whose mother's disorder was greatly improved during these eighteen months. She was not depressed, and nothing in particular distinguished her from the foster-parent group. Nor did her baby's emotional and physical growth show any striking differences.

But what of the other three? "Physical and emotional development . . . grossly deviant. Motor development . . . markedly retarded. . . . Did not sit up until 12 months of age, . . . rarely smiled, . . . frequent gastrointestinal upsets, . . . little spontaneous pleasure in her motor activities . . . and in her play with toys. . . . At age seven months . . . lost the ability to sit up after she had been capable of sitting for a month. . . . Quick to cry. Characterized by a somber stern expression." As the mothers became more depressed and withdrawn, so apparently did the babies. Two of these three disturbed children, after months of being moved about when their mothers had to be rehospitalized, have now settled down in good foster homes, and at two years and six months each appeared to be coming along nicely. Did they "learn" their temporarily disturbed behavior from the disturbed emotional climate? Far too early to say and far too small a sample (by the researcher's own admission), but again suggestive of a path needing further exploration.

Nonschizophrenic mothers of schizophrenic patients, much more easily located for research purposes, have been scrutinized, especially in the attempt to discover why one child becomes disturbed and others do not. The problem is far from final solution, but seemingly there is a pattern of submission to and dependence on mother among the psychotic children that is lacking in their brothers and sisters. One schizophrenic said: "My sister handled my mother by saying 'Boo' to her. . . . I didn't ignore my mother, so I had the nervous breakdown." And the sister of another felt that "the trouble is that I am not so dependent on my mother. . . . Erwin had a stronger attachment to my mother than I do. I don't think he could leave her."

This kind of relationship, presenting no great difficulty while the child is small, runs into trouble as he grows older. In most instances, society expects him to break away from the family, to be independent, to subject himself to the values and concerns of the outside world, but mother insists on clinging to the old relationship. The conflict that results can have disastrous consequences.

Sometimes, the reasons for differences in maternal—and paternal—attitudes can be pinpointed. The order of birth and the number in the family can affect behavior patterns, as we all know. We talk about the Eldest Son, the Only Daughter, the Baby of the Family, and we expect others to recognize the character almost as though it were a stereotype of fiction. Obviously, these variations in behavior are not genetically determined; the "baby" has no special set of genes to make him a spoiled brat. Although only a scattering of scientific work has been done on family size and the ordinal position of the individual, a study of more and less successful pilots in combat during the Korean conflict showed that an unusually high percentage of the successful men were later-born siblings. So too, as experimental subjects, college students from small families were more frightened than subjects from large families.

Looking at the situation from another point of view (and one that has been pursued for as many as thirty years with the same families), John Clausen has found that first-born children in American families are much more likely to achieve professional success than are their brothers and sisters. But they are less likely to be nonconformists, and they are less at ease socially than their siblings. He feels that these differences are connected with their view of their parents as representing all of society, whereas the later-born do not have this view and grow up relating more easily to other people and feeling more comfortable in social situations. This same thirty-year study indicates that sons tend to become emotionally unstable if their mothers represent both authority and affection for them. The son who is able to rebel against his father but retain his mother as a symbol of affection is in a very good situation, whereas the son who rebels against a mother who represents both love and power tends to become schizophrenic.

It is impossible to pretend that the research on disturbed families is as yet adequate to prove or disprove a specific theory of mental disorder; but as the evidence accumulates, the hereditary theory seems to lose ground. Much more work is needed, obviously, and much broader dissemination of its results. All the important psychiatric advances in the past ten years, with the exception of the tranquilizers, which are aids to treatment rather than sudden cures, involve recognition of the importance of the patient's environment. Lobotomy, shock therapy, and insulin coma are passé, but family therapy, group therapy, the therapeutic hospital community, and even house calls by psychotherapists are much in the forefront, whether laymen are aware of them or not. But they should be, for the new techniques not only explain the need for new research funds: they give hope and encouragement where there were none before. Genes are difficult to alter; the environment can be shaped by man.

CHAPTER 10

TODAY'S KNOWLEDGE

IN A SENSE—and that not a very precise one—the gene is to mental disorder as the bullet is to the total process of shooting a human being. No analogy can accurately convey my conceptualization of the role of heredity in schizophrenia or any other emotional disturbance, but because the bullet is, in reality, the active part of a total firearm, it must be clear that this position does not discount heredity entirely.

But the bullet is harmless without the cartridge, which in turn is useless without the gun, and at still another remove, there must be someone to fire the gun and a situation that calls for his doing so. It seems to me, therefore, that any "bullet theory" of firearms would necessarily be an oversimplification to the point of absurdity, and that too much attention has been paid to the possibly damaging effects of the bullet—or gene—when actually our concern is the total process in which the bullet—or gene—has a relevant part. But the gene, the hereditary factor, has not yet been isolated. Today we cannot distinguish, describe, or classify the "mental-disorder gene," and here the bullet analogy breaks down. Granting the inherited differences among human beings, however, we can leave the door open to the possibility of future discoveries.

Meanwhile, where do we stand? Already suggested in earlier chapters is the important relationship between ideas about the cause of mental disorders and the kinds of psychiatric treatment. A number of courses of action lie open to the psychiatrist, and the one he chooses may well be based not just on the patient but equally on the psychiatrist's own theories of causation. A young schizophrenic who might have an excellent prognosis in the proper hands is likely to be viewed with pessimistic gravity by a psychiatrist who assigns a strong role to heredity. This bias becomes all the more important if the patient's family shares it, and if they and psychiatrist form a coalition. Such a patient will be put into the hospital's maximum security ward and treated largely by electroshock or insulin drugs. This treatment may well convince him that he is hopeless, no good, and completely different from other people. If he improves and leaves the hospital, not only has he become adept at the "sick role," but his environment will respond to him as a convalescent of a special kind, and all his associations will be affected. His family, trying to be helpful, may caution him against getting out into the world again; after all, his heredity remains unchanged. In the long run, the patient may find that life in the psychiatric ward had some pleasant aspects.

Another patient with the same symptoms might be handled very differently by a psychiatrist who is impressed with the great adaptability of the human brain. He might not even be hospitalized, but seen (with his family) at home. Or the doctor might place him in a so-called therapeutic-community ward, where the emphasis is on personal responsibility and relations with other people and where there are no locks. Such a patient, when he leaves the hospital, has not been healing a broken mind in the way a fracture patient has mended his leg during his hospital stay; instead, he has been learning something about himself, and learning a repertoire of techniques which will serve him in the outside world as well as it did in the ward.

The whole question of heredity in mental disorders is no mere academic problem. Thanks especially to the work of sociologists, medicine is learning that predetermined attitudes have marked effects on the doctor's behavior toward his patients, the response of patients, and the treatment methods chosen. One basic tenet of medical philosophy has been that to treat a well patient as if he were sick is in no wise so serious an error as to treat a sick patient who has not been properly diagnosed. This was all right in the days when patients were seen as devilishly complex machines, but modern studies have taught us that great harm can be done by overdiagnosing and overtreating. In this connection, an important psychiatric lesson was learned in World War II that led to improvements during the Korean campaign. Fifteen percent of psychiatric casualties resulting from combat-zone stress were returned to combat duty during World War II. This figure was distressingly low, in spite of intensive care in clearing stations, field hospitals, and convalescent camps. It developed that the more the soldier was treated as if he had problems, the more quickly he was convinced that the limits of his combat durability had been reached. During the Korean conflict, on the other hand, great care was taken to treat psychiatric casualties as quickly as possible and as near the combat zone as possible, and it was heavily emphasized that the individual must not lose contact with his unit. The result was an unbelievable decrease in psychiatric cases who could not be returned to active duty.

The possible parallel lies between the behavior of the individual soldier away from his unit and the "sick" roles of the hospitalized patient. The "dangers" in each situation are nothing so simple as faking, malingering, or taking the easy way out, but a complex interactional pattern in which the individual is only one cog in the wheel. If one is treated as if he is sick, he usually obliges, and many factors, including the response he gets from his environment, are involved. If a patient is treated as if he is suffering from an incurable, chronic, mental defect, he will oblige in similar fashion.

Medical attitudes, hospital personnel, and even the public change with difficulty. For example, although writers on psychiatry in medical journals put great pressure on other physicians to behave toward the mentally disordered or emotionally upset in a tolerant, understanding fashion, most physicians subscribe to the theory of organic causation. No amount of learned writing in the journals has yet altered their basic position, in spite of their superficial knowledge. Not infrequently I receive a referral from another physician with an apologetic note saying that probably I can't do much anyhow because his patient is an example of poor protoplasm or bad stock. Although sometimes these terms are supposed to be funny, they nevertheless seem to represent an underlying attitude—and an unduly pessimistic one.

When the ordinary individual is sick in the ordinary hospital with a bodily illness or disorder, he wants to be taken care of. He regresses, feels more childlike, and needs extra attention, for both physical and emotional reasons. In the mental patient, possibly overprotected and usually restricted in his social activities before he ever enters the hospital, such treatment can only continue and reinforce unhealthy tendencies. Physicians, nurses, and ward attendants may be so steeped in the classic medical tradition that they approach the mental patient as they would the sick patient and limit his opportunities for improvement at the outset. It is the sociologists, interestingly, who have been laboring mightily to point out that within the psychiatric hospital itself there may be untherapeutic attitudes that keep the patients "sick," sometimes by duplicating the attitudes and situations he faced at home.

Of course, most of us in psychiatry have occasionally found

it difficult to communicate with a particular patient, and ended the interview by offering him a tranquilizer. It is almost as if the doctor said, "Although I can't function in one role, I can rely on my traditional role to achieve a relationship with you." But this situation, occurring infrequently, is not motivated by any underlying confusion about ultimate treatment. Nor is it equivalent to the situation that occurs every day in the office of the psychiatrist who believes that mental disorders are primarily organic, and therefore that pills are the most reliable agents. Like the believer in heredity, he leaves his patient alone and untreated in large areas of his disturbed world.

For physicians and laymen alike, one of the great hindrances to accepting the importance of human interaction in producing emotional disturbances has been their difficulty in attributing that much power to those relationships. After all, we have families, know other people, and get along quite well—or so the surface argument may run. Perhaps underneath there is hidden fear, an ability to ignore (just as many persons simply never think about enemy bombs), or, in some instances, a lack of information. Many physicians, for example, find it almost impossible to recognize the influence of their personalities, as distinguished from their treatment techniques, on the recovery of their patients. Many parents have no idea of their impact on their children. And, of course, if influence and impact produce unhappy results, all the more reason to forget or deny their effectiveness.

Even the professional convinced of the power of human relationships has to admit that work has only begun in this vast field and that some of the work already done has already been modified by subsequent research—all in little more than ten years. At this time, three generalizations seem to be valid, and they may serve to represent the direction of present-day thinking.

First, more than one type of family is capable of producing disturbed emotions and severe mental distress. ("Momism" and "the schizophrenogenic mother" have been abandoned as attention has broadened to take in father and his role, in relation to both child and mother.)

Second, social order—that is, the socioeconomic class to which the family belongs—has an important part in the way family members relate to and interact with each other, but not with the frequency or degree of mental disorder. (The drift hypothesis and the breeder hypothesis have recently been brought into doubt by new and more accurate statistics.)

Third, families in which severe mental disturbance occurs have serious problems of communication as either one pair or the entire group wittingly or unwittingly confuse and mislead each other. (The double-bind hypothesis has been expanded to include more than mother-child interaction.)

More particularly, I think it safe to say that the family studies of severe emotional disorders agree on the following conclusions:

Although usually only one patient is identified within the family (that is, the individual who is first brought to a psychiatrist or to a social agency or to a hospital), close investigation reveals that the parents and siblings as well suffer some degree of disturbance.

Overall, families with severe emotional disorders reveal more of the following traits than do other families: (1) a tendency to be upwardly mobile and dissatisfied with their current status, whatever it may be; (2) a tendency to make frequent geographical moves not explained by the father's job changes and/or a tendency to be on the fringe of their own subculture, be it a neighborhood group, kinship group, or whatever; (3) a tendency toward broken homes (that is, divorce or desertion); (4) a preponderance of severe parental illness (or death), resulting in the absence of the usual parent-child relationship; (5) a tendency toward either great and obvious disharmony or covert but still apparent distance between the parents, which results in the child's lack of a model for warm human relationships; (6) the tendency of one other member of the family (at least) to show increasing emotional disturbance if the identified patient improves as a result of psychiatric treatment (a phenomenon technically referred to as "family homeostasis," and proof of the complicated ties between family members and the involvement of more than one individual in the mental disorder); (7) the identification of the patient by the family as a result of any of a number of factors including ordinal position among the children, circumstances before and surrounding birth, and sex (a fact about family compositions that some studies have failed to take into account).

These are not hereditary factors, but after one has worked with families, it is difficult, for many reasons, to accept the hereditary hypothesis of severe mental disorders. Among others, it is hard to imagine a hereditary disorder that would affect so many members of the same family and, at the same time, affect them in such different forms. A genetic hypothesis that would cover all the ramification of most family situations would be so broad as to be meaningless. Furthermore, if schizophrenia, for example, runs in families, it runs in very few families, even by the geneticists' own estimates.

On the other hand, meeting a truly nurturing and healthy family is a truly impressive experience, and it is difficut to imagine what kind of hereditary handicap this kind of family could not overcome. That biological equipment is but a small part of living has been proved by Helen Keller and her magnificent and patient teacher. There is no reason to imagine, for example, that a child born with a "sensitive nervous system" (if indeed one can be) could not be protected during his formative years by parents who accepted their responsibilities and were able to give.

But most geneticists do not claim that the symptoms of the mentally disturbed are uninfluenced by environment, and only an occasional organicist claims that people break down without any extraordinary external stress. Actually, there is little reason to doubt that nature and nurture in some ways interact, but neither the susceptibility nor the environmental causative factor is enough in itself. Mental disorders, however, seem so complex that the model of physical illness is insufficient, if not downright misleading. For example, there is still the problem of what mental disorder is (please note again the absence of the term "mental illness") and how discretely and distinctly these disorders may be classified. Much genetic research depends on diagnosis; and diagnosis in psychiatry is variable, local, changing, even for the same individual. The statistics cannot account for the fact that the longer an individual remains in a mental hospital, the more likely he is to be labeled "schizophrenic."

There is, furthermore, the problem of the complex human being, his astoundingly adaptive brain, and his myriad influences. A single day in the life of one civilized human being defies adequate description. Whether he is being bombarded by biological urges, television, his mother-in-law, the unspoken fear of having a hydrogen bomb go off, or his relentless competition to make more money, he is constantly and unceasingly the victim of forces that are not always well defined. Our recent beginnings in the area of social psychiatry and sociology would indicate that these forces are many times more significant for the production of mental disorders than those the biologists espouse.

From the opposite point of view, we have raised the question of whether biological defects are enough to produce the individual's social breakdown. It must be noted that the years of greatest susceptibility to mental disorder are those associated not so much with biological changes as with social changes—first the years of courtship, marriage, child rearing, and job advancement, and then the years of dissolution of the family, retirement, and lowered social status.

Furthermore, the action of heredity on emotional development may take the form of what has been called "negative selection." That is, certain inherited characteristics are rejected in certain family settings. The child born with an adequate but not outstanding mind is going to be a disappointment to parents bent on producing an atomic scientist. Or a listless baby may acquire a label from which he will never escape. Jane (whom we met in Chapter 8) heard her mother say, "You have always tried to interfere between me and your father for the past twenty years," and this before she had had her twentieth birthday. But then mother went on to describe the infant as quite active, often requiring a trip to the pediatrician because of bruises acquired when she miraculously got out of her crib. Such childish "activity" may be attributed (in part, at least) to biological characteristics, and obviously this mother must have felt helpless when faced with them, unable to contain the baby and prevent her from hurting herself. Perhaps in this type of situation it is impossible to determine cause and effect precisely, but certainly mother, referring to a brief period, encompasses her daughter's entire lifetime and indeed a few months *in utero*. Jane's busy exploits continue to influence her mother's attitude—her negative selection of activity. They become a kind of trademark of disturbance. In another family, Jane might have been accepted as normal—and remained so.

Once Jane and other patients have been diagnosed, another factor enters the picture: their probable hospitalization and its effects. The bulk of genetic and biochemical studies have been done on hospitalized mental patients as we have seen, and these studies may be exceedingly misleading because of the nature of the institution itself. The hospital routine changes behavior and biochemical makeup alike, although the extent to which it may affect them is difficult for the layman to conceive. The patient is taught the patient's role, deprived of his possessions, his contacts with the outside, and his previous ego-enhancing activities; in fact, he may eventually be deprived of his identity. It is not surprising, therefore, to find slight biochemical differences between mental patients and medical students. Such extreme changes can easily produce variations in some of his blood components or organ systems. And he may drink more coffee, too!

Appreciation of the extent of the hospital's influence on the patient has focused attention on correcting the detrimental effects and implementing the therapeutic ones. The results of the open doors can be shown by comparing total number of discharges to admissions and by noting the relatively slight emphasis on insulin, electroshock, or the tranquilizing drugs. Instead, there is now great emphasis on follow-up clinics and house visits by the psychiatrists; once the patient is discharged, he is not forgotten. This new policy also recognizes the importance of the patient's family for his well-being, in or out of the hospital.

The older forms of treatment, so much more closely related to physiological theories of mental disorder, are, as we have seen, less and less popular. Even the newest tranquilizer must be used quickly while it still works. "The era of [electric] shock therapy is fast drawing to a close," according to a recent survey of techniques. The use of insulin, which once encouraged theories about carbohydrate metabolism and schizophrenia, seems of doubtful value now that it has been proved that insulin comas have no advantage over barbituate-induced comas and probably less, even though the barbituates were used only for a control group, and are known to be unsatisfactory in producing cures.

The lobotomy is virtually a thing of the past, but its story is representative of the sudden acceptance and sudden decline of a particular form of treatment. In 1936 a Portuguese neurosurgeon named Moniz reported that he had cut through some of the principal nervous pathways in the frontal portion of the cerebral hemisphere, first in monkeys and then in a few human beings, and had achieved striking results in relieving the most severe symptoms of schizophrenia. The operation was picked up quickly, with more enthusiasm than good sense, and within a few years thousands of lobotomies were being done all over the country. For a time (as might be expected) reports were highly satisfactory. Wild madmen given to murderous rages were emerging from the operation as meek as lambs and without significant intellectual impairment. Of course, some died, and some got convulsions; but all in all these early reports were very impressive. They also led to theories about schizophrenia, the most popular being that schizophrenia represented an imbalance between the old brain (archepallium) and the new brain (neopallium).

A recent report from England provides what is probably the final chapter in this saga. In 1,000 lobotomy cases, the mortality rate was 6 percent. Recovery or improvement was claimed in one-third of the cases, but 10 percent of them subsequently relapsed. Some patients developed uremic states or more complex metabolic disorders; and nearly all, even those who were counted as recovered, showed inability to profit by experience and plan ahead, reduction of activity, lack of spontaneity, and persistent lack of abstract thought. Today only a few lobotomies are being done, and most of those are to correct the intractable pain of chronic cancer.

During the popularity of this or any other form of biological treatment, there are always a few voices crying in the wilderness, pointing out that there is little to go on but enthusiasm, that these patients are receiving more attention from doctors and nursing staff, and that the treatment itself may have little to do with any improvement. This is not to say that a doctor sold on the efficacy of, say, insulin might not be able to sell his patient and his patient's family on the idea and produce improvement by virtue not of the chemical therapy but of the interpersonal relationships necessarily involved in the course of treatment. And so we return to the power of human interaction.

Once more let it be said that nature and nurture constantly interact: a genetic theory and a social theory need not be mutually exclusive. If such linkage is assumed, social pressures are going to affect the "weak" more than the "strong." But the influence of heredity on mental disorder has been so ingrained in the thinking of the public and the medical profession that, if only to arrive eventually at some kind of balance, it seems necessary to consider the proposition that mental disorders can have an entirely social cause. Even this proposition does not ignore genetically endowed differences between individuals, but it does not assign them a causative role. It assumes that genetic differences between individuals (for example, "intelligence" or "temperament") are important *only* in relation to the social interaction between people. Years of research will be needed to establish the subtleties of the nature-nurture interaction. There is much to be done by both biological scientists and behavioral scientists, but there is absolutely no reason why their results should not be combined when we come to look for answers to the complex nature-nurture question.

CHAPTER 11

TOMORROW'S POSSIBILITIES

MUCH HAS been said about the need for sympathetic, understanding, permissive treatment of the emotionally disturbed. The more time, money, and constructive care put into a hospital ward or an outpatient clinic, the more schizophrenics returned to useful life. We have seen that the patient in the state hospital who looks, acts, and talks in a strange way may be largely the product of the social isolation and the peculiar milieu in which he lives. To remove the "insane" from society and to house them in an asylum many miles from town may very well create a group of infrahuman beings unless drastic changes are made. Meanwhile the fate of these men and women is in the powerful hands of a relatively few people—lawyers, judges, and psychiatrists. Often, even the families are helpless against the orders of the court, however reluctant they may be to see father, mother, or child sent to that ancient and brooding fortress miles from familiar surroundings.

But fear of mental disorder is far from being conquered, and those who are afraid of a more liberal policy must be adequately answered when they ask: What will keep crazy people from getting out and unleashing their insanity against society? What will keep a murderer, especially one with a clever lawyer and an unscrupulous psychiatrist, from going free again just because he claims he didn't know what he was doing?

In answer to the first question: It does happen, but not very often. Enough occasional newspaper stories about the crime of an escaped patient keep the pot boiling with no attention to the much higher crime rate per capita among other people. Recently, for example, a patient escaped from a Veterans Administration Hospital. All patients were denied privileges, and an extensive investigation was demanded and conducted, heralded by the arrival of representatives from Washington, D.C., in the first available plane. Yet the chief of police, quite unassociated with the hospital, had long been pointing out to fearful and irate citizens that proportionately more crime of all kinds was committed in their city by individuals who had never been in any mental hospital than it was by past or present residents of this single institution. The fear of criminal acts may not be unjustified, but it would seem to be definitely misplaced.

To the second question, there is no clear-cut answer yet. The so-called McNaughton rule by which an individual is judged sane or insane (in order to be ruled not guilty by reason of insanity) depends on knowing right from wrong—not always the easiest distinction for anyone to make. This black-and-white differentiation stems from the old feeling that the mentally "sick" were completely unlike us, the mentally "healthy." The possible shades of gray are ignored, as are the possible degrees of emotional balance or disturbance; but until the public, who are afraid of finding themselves somewhere along this continuum instead of solidly at the "healthy" extreme, are reassured and their fright is allayed, the clever and unscrupulous professional may very well continue his present course. In other words, this particular problem is caught up in a circle of fears that certainly deserve respectful attention.

One answer, presently in use by twenty-six states in the United States and also in many foreign countries, is legal sterilization of persons declared insane. But, in a sense, this is no answer at all, for it simply returns us to the definition of "insane," the separation of "right" and "wrong," and the pessimistic attitude toward mental disorder that seems unnecessary in this day and age. Who is to say that any particular schizophrenic is forever incapable of leading a healthy life again? One group who would fail even to recognize the point of the question are, of course, the convinced believers in the hereditary hypotheses—"once in the genes, always in the genes." If the major mental disorders were genetically caused, sterilization might eventually breed them out of the population, and schizophrenia would be no more. But until there is further and much more conclusive proof, are we justified in such action? Like indiscriminate incarceration, reckless sterilization raises the larger specter of some as yet unknown power group some day using these weapons, so conveniently at hand, for their own purposes. "Who is to say that tomorrow it may not be I?"

An even broader question also affects the future possibilities, not only of the disturbed, but the rest of mankind as well: What of eugenics and the whole body of theory, idealistic and practical, that has grown up around it?

The famous geneticist and Nobel Prize winner H. J. Muller wrote *Out of the Night* some twenty-five years ago, because he felt that through proper selection, it was possible to create a race of men who would be free of ignorance and superstition, full of wisdom, creativeness, stable temperament, and joy in living. This is a situation devoutly to be desired, but it is a situation that does not bear much scrutiny. Who is to determine what are desirable traits? Who is to say what kind of joy we are to breed for, even if it were possible to establish that joy is a hereditary trait? Those who love the classics may hate jazz. How does one define emotional stability, and how is it differentiated from the kind of plebeian dullness that kills many an otherwise promising dinner party?

Charles Darwin published *On the Origin of Species* in 1859, and his abilities need no defense. Yet this genius was also a shy man who lived to a ripe old age with almost constant and crippling hypochondriasis, and there is little evidence that he was emotionally stable or full of joy. Who, then, would venture to sacrifice one of the most significant treatises in human history? What of William Blake? Charles Lamb? Wagner? Da Vinci? Dostoevski?

But Muller has not abandoned his idea, and in recent years he has more than once proposed that the United States should institute selective breeding—now as a defense against the dangers of the modern world. Our patriotism must overcome our squeamishness about the mechanics of it. He offers no very detailed plan, but is cautious enough to advocate specifically that the sperm of great men be kept in a deep-freeze for decades. Such an arrangement would permit long-range assessment of their worth and "their latent genetic potentials," as well as avoiding snap judgments based on current fads. He has never offered much, if anything, however, about positive means of identifying superior genes, implying only that "great men" have them.

Suppose that Congress approved such a program, and a body of eminent scientists was appointed to decide what traits should be chosen. Would they agree on standards of beauty or adequate and desirable size? Would they be able to state which intelligence tests measure adequately, and could they differentiate between what we call intelligence and the effects of schooling, culture, and so on? Would they agree on what racial stocks should be promulgated because of their desirable characteristics? Would they sacrifice a Marian Anderson for some lesser voice and a different skin color?

Furthermore, who would raise these gene-bank children generations hence? Muller believes that there is no such thing as paternal instinct, inherent pride in one's own genetic material. Although it is true that some primitive peoples have no knowledge that the male plays a role in the production of the progeny, much less any conception of genetic material or genes, Muller is advocating the improvement of *our* stock, not that of some primitive tribe. If he feels that fathers of children produced by artificial insemination have no problems connected with their lack of biological participation, he has talked to few if any psychiatrists. We might very well have to breed a special race of fathers before the gene bank could begin to be useful.

Interest in improving the race is far from new, however, extending back at least to the sixth century before our era and possibly even before. Plato, perhaps the most serious and best-known eugenicist until the nineteenth century, stated in the Fifth Book of *The Republic* as a cardinal principle that the ideal state should be perpetuated by the marriage of courage and beauty. The brave should wed the fair, and only the brave should the fair choose. Only such marriages would be allowed, regulated by the state, not by the will of the parties, and performed only at state-appointed seasons and in groups for the sake of economy. Bridegrooms and brides would be mated by lot, and the lots would be officially manipulated to bring together superior persons of each sex, whose offspring, known as children of the state, would, for all practical purposes, be raised by the state instead of the actual parents. Inferior persons might mate, but their offspring would be done away with. Although this theory, whether serious or not, is repugnant to those with democratic feelings, it must be said that Plato had definite qualities in mind—"fair" and "brave."

Modern eugenics, associated chiefly with Sir Francis Galton, stems naturally from the Darwinian theory of evolution and is well suited to the notion of the survival of the fittest. Because the stresses of modern society are not really known, however, it is not easy to say who is fittest. Big muscles are unnecessary when one can carry a gun or call a policeman. Superior intellect is of no special value when there is a crying need for manual labor. Even the feeblest of the very young and the very old are almost always kept from starvation by state or county or city.

A further complication lies in the fact that the qualities of the human being that we call "personality traits" and "emotions" are not necessarily simple, easily delimited entities. The psychologist and the psychiatrist are constantly aware of the convolutions and variations, either in the experimental laboratory or the doctor's office. But most eugenicists do not admit such complexities of behavior and insist on seeing racial improvement strictly in terms of good and evil. Many such individuals have been old-time biologists and geneticists, not well acquainted with the more recent work done on social learning, social structure, and learning contexts. Often, members of modern eugenic societies, after advocating the eradication of certain obvious and quite rare medical disorders, speak only of "race betterment" without having anything to say about what should be bettered. Recently, Salvador Luria of MIT and Guido Pontecorvo of the University of Glasgow added their voices to Muller's: "Social and ethical effects of purposeful management of human evolution could be as far-reaching as those experienced in the development of nuclear fission," according to the newspaper account of their statement. Again, no details, but we can hope that the "effects" are for good rather than evil (to revert to the usual eugenic terminology).

There should be nothing but support, of course, for those who would like to control *proved* hereditary disorders by discouraging affected individuals from procreating or by educating them in the selection of a mate. Other considerations, however, suggest the greatest caution. Many of the ideas propounded by eugenicists have not been established scientifically, as we have seen in the area of the causation of severe mental disorders. And medical science has found methods of handling many other genetic disorders so that they no longer impair the development of the race. There is no reason to believe that even more methods having full or partial genetic base cannot be similarly handled in the future. Many of the world's greatest scientists and statesmen have been affected by diabetes, but now since the discovery of insulin and special diet, they can lead normal lives. Should we risk the destruction of other men like them?

The overwhelming social problems that face us and our relative ignorance in so many areas of culture and human interaction require a century of research, public information, and education. Instead of making eugenics an immediate necessity, they seem to render eugenic notions premature if not implausible. Even on a simple level, one of the difficulties of remaining objective about human nature and/or nurture is the fact that there has crept into our language a way of speaking about people that itself makes us think in hereditary terminology. We commonly say that so and so takes after his father or that a two-year-old is a night owl and thus resembles his grandmother. We cut across the actual, immediate situation as well as the child's earlier learning experiences and focus in an oversimplified way merely for simplicity's sake: baby and grandma are both early risers; therefore, baby gets or "inherits" this behavior pattern or personality trait from her. A way of speaking inclines us to forget that two parents and three other grandparents are involved, that in two years baby has learned much, and that the whole is greater than the parts. Actually, no one has demonstrated that such traits are hereditary, and possibly we do ourselves and our children harm by thinking toward the past rather than the future. If, given new awareness of such holdovers in daily life and further information about present-day knowledge, we can begin instead to look ahead, we must find a focus for future study, whether it is professional experimentation or public enlightenment.

Surely it is apparent to those who face the facts that man's inhumanity to man is the principal problem ahead—whether one chooses to think of it in terms of psychiatry, sociology, religion, World War III—or the incidence of schizophrenia. But as we are coming to realize, a single choice may be unwise (although any thought is obviously better than none). The complexity of the problem and the need for a multidisciplinary approach have, I hope, become clear by now. The ills of the soul have passed from priest and physician to all of science, because it is these ills that threaten mankind more than predatory beasts, deadly parasites, or wildly multiplying cells. In the psychiatric realm, the magnificent contributions of Freud, having paved the way, left little truly startling that one man alone might produce. Now the very deficiencies of our research make it painfully apparent that exploitation of mankind's emotional problems requires the combined efforts of psychiatrist, psychologist, psychiatric nurse, social worker, sociologist, anthropologist, economist, mathematician, and probably many more.

The shift away from the idea of "one mental illness" has robbed the psychiatrist of his hierarchial ability to pronounce: "You are insane." The concept of a continuum from normality to neuroticism to psychosis has emphasized the importance of all data gathered by students of human behavior, whether that behavior is "normal," "healthy," "sick," or as yet unclassified. The emphasis on interaction among human beings has dissolved the walls of the psychiatrist's office and made him and his patient a part of the community, the subgroup, the culture, and the world.

In some ways, this dissolution will make the future more difficult for us all. We continue to make judgments about the relative degree of an individual's "sickness," knowing very little about anything but the extremes of the continuum: actually we have no standard of the "normal" to use as a yardstick. Although the public has been deluged with advice on raising children, astonishingly little relevant information exists about the ordinary family and how they do it. But the public is addicted to the concept of "normal" and the belief in a normal versus an abnormal personality. This belief goes much deeper than the influence of "How to Raise Your Child" books. Expert and layman are both caught up in historical and psychological factors that tend to make us dichotomize normal and abnormal.

We live in an era of classification, and the desire to categorize and delineate all human endeavor ranges from botany to one's income. Classifications are attempted in order to simplify, and, in the natural-history stage of any science, they are an essential. Because it is easy to spot somebody who is "crazy" and contrast him with somebody who is "sane," personalities seem to be easily classified, too. But these easy distinctions represent only a few percent at each end of the continuum from mental health to mental disorder, and they do not take care of the bulk of the rest of us, who fall somewhere in between. Still, the process goes on, partly, at least, because classification supports the old feeling that one's own group must be superior to some other group.

Certain other human tendencies play a part in this wish of ours to separate "normal" from "abnormal" personalities. If one assumes that the truly abnormal are produced by hereditary cells, he does not need to feel much guilt about man's inhumanity to these men. If poverty is inherited, what need to feed the poor? If ignorance is a genetic fact, why supply adequate schools and teachers? Actually, if the truly abnormal are completely different from the rest of us, it makes sense to isolate them in what we euphemistically call "state hospitals."

In addition, if the "normal" is a valid concept, then those who consider themselves normal can be sure where they stand. If it is not, then how can one know where he stands in comparison to others? In a competitive, acquisitive society like ours, this measuring-up, this classification, is very important. It is important to insecure people, too, because they can label their behavior right, or "normal," instead of the much more accurate but less reassuring "conventional."

It would be conveniently tidy to be able to split all the world—or even our own personal worlds—into "normal" and "abnormal," a split that also implies right and wrong, but when one looks at actual studies of ordinary people, especially the few studies of ordinary families, there is little reason to cling to our earlier assumptions. For example, there seem to be so many different styles of family living and so many different child-rearing practices that it is meaningless to say that spanking is or is not a good thing. There are families whom one would prefer to be with on Christmas Day and others on New Year's Eve, but this is not to say which is the better family. There are parents who appear to live harmoniously together but whose children are nervous, and other parents who get along miserably but whose children appear to be functioning quite well. They are all ordinary families.

On that day when it is generally recognized that "normality" is a myth, that mankind does not divide into sane and insane, that mental disorder is not an intractable, unalterable ogre unrelated to ordinary human nature, we will look with more optimism toward the future. We will recognize that man is fantastically adaptable (especially when he is given adequate opportunities) and that most people contribute something to the world. We will know that men and women, strangers or neighbors, are not "less normal" or "more inferior" than we are—just different.

1. YOUR PROBLEM AND MINE

SROLE, LEO, and others. *Mental Health in the Metropolis.* New York: McGraw-Hill, 1962.

TAIT, A. C., and W. T. MCCLATCHEY. "Initial Psychiatric Illness in Involutional Women: I. Clinical Aspects," *Journal of Mental Science,* 103 (1957), 132–45.

2. THE SUBNORMAL BRAIN AND THE SUPRANORMAL BRAIN

BAILEY, NANCY. "A New Look at the Curve of Intelligence," in *Proceedings of the 1956 Invitational Conference on Testing Problems.* Princeton: Educational Testing Service, 1956.

BRAIN, WALTER RUSSELL. *Some Reflections on Genius.* Philadelphia: Lippincott, 1961.

BURKS, BARBARA S. "On the Relative Contributions of Nature and Nurture to Average Group Differences in Intelligence," *Proceedings of the National Academy of Science,* 24 (1938), 276–82.

DAVIS, RUSSELL, and NORMA KENT. "Intellectual Development in School-Children with Special Reference to Family Background," *Proceedings of the Royal Society of Medicine,* 48 (1955), 993–95.

HARRELL, RUTH F., and others. "The Influence of Vitamin Supplementation of the Diets of Pregnant and Lactating Women on the Intelligence of Their Offspring," *Metabolism*, 5 (1956), 555–62.

HILGARD, E. R. *Introduction to Psychology*. 2d. ed. New York: Harcourt, Brace, 1959.

KAELBING, R., J. B. CRAIG, and B. PASAMANICK. "Urinary Porphobilinogen: Results of Screening 2,500 Psychiatric Patients," *Archives of General Psychiatry*, 5 (1961), 494–508.

New York Times, June 27, 1960, p. 1.

PASAMANICK, BENJAMIN. "Research on the Influence of Sociocultural Variables upon Organic Factors in Mental Retardation," *American Journal of Mental Deficiency*, 64 (1959), 316–20.

PENROSE, L. S. *Outline of Human Genetics*. New York: Wiley, 1959.

Report on 200 Families Receiving Aid to Needy Children. Santa Clara County (California) Welfare Department.

WEISBERG, PAUL S., and K. J. SPRINGER. "Environmental Factors in Creative Function: Study of Gifted Children," *Archives of General Psychiatry*, 5 (1961), 554–64.

3. THOSE POPULAR GENES

BÖÖK, JAN A. "Genetical Aspects of Schizophrenic Psychoses," in *The Etiology of Schizophrenia*. New York: Basic Books, 1960.

CRAIKE, W. H., and E. SLATER. "Folie à deux in Uniovular Twins Reared Apart," *Brain*, 68 (1945), 213.

ESSEN-MÖLLER, W. "Psychiatrische Untersuchungen an einer Serie von Zwillingen," *Acta psychiat. et neurol.*, Supplement 23, 1941.

FREEDMAN, D. G. "Some Effects on Personality of Prenatal Developmental Events in a Pair of Genetically Identical Twins," paper presented to the Western Psychological Association, April, 1959.

JACKSON, DON D. "A Critique of the Literature on the Genetics of Schizophrenia," in *The Etiology of Schizophrenia*. New York: Basic Books, 1960.

KALLMANN, F. J. *Genetics of Schizophrenia*. Locust Valley, N.Y.: Augustin, 1938.

———. *Heredity in Health and Mental Disorder*. New York: W. W. Norton, 1953.

LUXENBERGER, H. "Untersuchung an schizophrenen Zwillingen und ihren Geschwistern zur Prüfung der Realität von Manifestationschwankungen," *Ztschr. Neurol. u. Psychiat.*, 154 (1936).

MESNIKOFF, ALVIN M., and others. "Intrafamilial Determinants of Divergent Sexual Behavior in Twins," paper presented to the Toronto Psychiatric Association, May, 1962.

NEEL, J. V., and W. J. SCHULL. *Human Heredity*. Chicago: University of Chicago Press, 1954.

PENROSE, L. S. *Outline of Human Genetics*. New York: Wiley, 1959.

RAASCHOU-NIELSEN, ELISABETH, reported in *Danish Medical Bulletin*, 7 (June, 1960), 82.

4. THE GENES ACCUSED

BENDER, LAURETTA. "Genetic Data in Evaluation and Management of Disordered Behavior in Children," *Diseases of the Nervous System*, Monograph Supplement 21, 1960.

ELDRED, S. H., N. W. BELL, and L. J. SHERMAN. "A Pilot Study Comparing the Effects of Pineal Extract and a Placebo in Patients with Chronic Schizophrenia," *New England Journal of Medicine*, 263 (1960), 1330–35.

ERNST, K. " 'Geordnete Familienverhältnisse' späterer Schizophrener im Lichte einer Nachuntersuchung," *Arch. Psychiat.*, 194 (1956).

KALLMANN, F. J. *Heredity in Health and Mental Disorder*. New York: Norton, 1953.

KANNER, L. "To What Extent Is Early Infantile Autism Determined by Constitutional Inadequacies?" *A Res. Nerv. & Ment. Dis. Proc.*, 33 (1954).

KETY, SEYMOUR S. "Recent Biochemical Theories of Schizophrenia," in *The Etiology of Schizophrenia*. New York: Basic Books, 1960.

KOLB, LAWRENCE. Report to the Annual Meeting of the American Psychoanalytic Association, 1960.

LANG, T. "Studies on the Genetic Determination of Homosexuality," *Journal of Nervous and Mental Diseases*, 92 (1940), 55–64.

LUNDBY, P. "Incidence of Schizophrenia in a Group of Norwegian Seamen," *Acta psychiat. et neurol.*, 30 (1955).

MAYER-GROSS, W. *Clinical Psychiatry*. Baltimore: Williams & Wilkins.

MONEY, J., and others. "Hermaphroditism," *Johns Hopkins Hospital Bulletin*, 97 (1955), 284–300.

PENROSE, L. S. *Outline of Human Genetics*. New York: Wiley, 1959.

RAINER, J. D., and others. "Homosexuality and Heterosexuality in Identical Twins," *Psychosomatic Medicine*, 22 (1960), 251–59.

RANDELL, JOHN B., reported in *Medical Tribune*, March 13, 1961.

SCHWABE, A. D., and others. "Pubertal Feminization in a Genetic Male with Testicular Atrophy and Normal Urinary Gonadotropin," *Journal of Clinical Endocrinology*, 22 (1962), 839–45.

SHELDON, W. H. *The Varieties of Human Physique*. New York: Harper, 1940.

SLATER, E. *Psychotic and Neurotic Illnesses in Twins*, Medical Research Council, Special Report No. 278. London: H.M. Stationery Office, 1953.

STOLLER, ROBERT J., and A. C. ROSEN, "The Intersexed Patient," *California Medicine*, 91 (1959), 261–65.

TERRY, GLADYS C., and THOMAS A. C. RENNIE. *Analysis of Pargasia*. Nervous and Mental Disease Monograph Series, No. 64. New York: Nervous and Mental Disease Publishing Company, n.d.

WEINER, A. S. "Blood-Groups and Disease," *Lancet*, 1 (1962), 813–16.

5. A SALK VACCINE FOR THE MIND?

Acta Psychiatrica et Neurologica Scandinavica, Supplement, Helsinki, 1961.

BEECHER, H. "The Powerful Placebo," *Journal of the American Medical Association*, 159 (1955), 1602–6.

HEATH, ROBERT G. "A Biochemical Hypothesis on the Etiology of Schizophrenia," in *The Etiology of Schizophrenia*. New York: Basic Books, 1960.

HOLLISTER, LEE E., reported in *Medical News,* April 21, 1961.

HUXLEY, ALDOUS. *The Doors of Perception.* New York: Harper, 1954.

KETY, SEYMOUR S. "Recent Biochemical Theories of Schizophrenia," in *The Etiology of Schizophrenia.* New York: Basic Books, 1960.

KURLAND, A. A., "The Drug Placebo—Its Psychodynamic and Conditional Reflex Action," *Behavioral Science,* 2 (1957), 101–10.

LIEF, H. I. "The Effects of Taraxein on a Patient in Analysis," *Archives of Neurology and Psychiatry,* 78 (1957).

LORANGER, ARMAND W., and others. "The Placebo Effect in Psychiatric Drug Research," *Journal of the American Medical Association,* 176 (1961), 118–23.

MANN, J. D., and E. H. LABROSSE. "The Urinary Excretion of Phenolic Acids by Normal and Schizophrenic Males," *Archives of General Psychiatry,* 1 (1959).

SANTOS, L., and M. GROSS. "The Clinical Effect of Norethandrolone on Incontinent Mental Patients' Action Induced by Non-Verbal Communication," *American Journal of Psychiatry,* 118 (1961), 223–26.

WOOLLEY, D. WAYNE, reported in *Medical News,* April 21, 1961.

WRIGHT, W. W., in *American Journal of Psychiatry,* 5 (1926), 365.

YUWILER, A., and others. "Serum Oxidase Tests and Schizophrenia," *Archives of General Psychiatry,* 4 (April, 1961), 395–403.

6. IN THE MIDDLE OF THE MILIEU

BENEDICT, PAUL K., and IRVING JACKS. "Mental Illness in Primitive Societies," *Psychiatry,* 17 (1954), 377–89.

HARVEY, WILLIAM. "Changing Syndrome and Culture," *International Journal of Social Psychiatry,* 2 (1956), 165–71.

KIMMICH, ROBERT A., "Ethnic Aspects of Schizophrenia in Hawaii," *Psychiatry,* 23 (1960), 97–103.

LIN TSUNG-YI. "A Study of the Incidence of Mental Disorder in

Chinese and Other Cultures," *Psychiatry*, 16 (1953), 313–36.

LISTWAN, IGNANCY A. "Mental Disorders in Migrants," *Medical Journal of Australia*, 1 (1959), 566–68.

MURPHY, H. B., "Culture and Mental Disorder in Singapore," in *Culture and Mental Health: Cross-cultural Studies*, ed. M. K. Opler. New York: Macmillan, 1959.

Review and Newsletter No. 9: Special Issue on Schizophrenia. Montreal: McGill University, 1960. (Reports by E. D. Whittkower and others; E. F. B. Forster; David McAllester and Kei Hirano Howes; Arthur J. Prange.)

7. CLOSER TO HOME

CHRISTENSON, W. N., and L. E. HINKLE. "Differences in Illness and Prognosis Signs in Two Groups of Young Men," *Journal of the American Medical Association*, 177 (1961), 247–53.

EATON, J. W., and R. J. WEIL. *Culture and Mental Disorders.* Glencoe: Free Press, 1955.

HINKLE, L. E., and H. G. WOLFF. "The Nature of Man's Adaptation to His Total Environment and the Relation of This to Illness," *Archives of Internal Medicine*, 99 (1957), 442 ff.

HOLLINGSHEAD, A. B., and F. C. REDLICH. *Social Class and Mental Illness.* New York: Wiley, 1958.

IZIKOWITZ, reported in *Medical Tribune*, October 9, 1961.

KOLONOFF, H., and others. "A Longitudinal Study of Schizophrenia," *American Journal of Psychiatry*, 117 (1960), 348.

LEIGHTON, ALEXANDER H. *My Name Is Legion.* New York: Basic Books, 1959.

PLANK, R. "Ecology of Schizophrenia," *American Journal of Orthopsychiatry*, 29 (1959).

SEELEY, JOHN R., and others. *Crestwood Heights.* New York: Basic Books, 1956.

SOMMER, ROBERT. "Visitors to Mental Hospitals," *Mental Hygiene*, 33 (January, 1959).

ZUBECK, J. P., and others. "Electroencephalographic Changes During and After 14 Days of Perceptual Deprivation," *Science*, 139 (1963), 490–2.

STIERLIN, HELM. "The Adaptation to the 'Stronger' Person's Reality," *Psychiatry*, 22 (1959), 146.

YI-CHUANG LU. "Mother-Child Role Relations in Schizophrenia," *Psychiatry*, 24 (1961), 133–42.

10. TODAY'S KNOWLEDGE

ACKNER, BRIAN, A. HARRIS, and A. J. OLDHAM. "Insulin Treatment of Schizophrenia: A Controlled Study," *Lancet*, 1 (1957), 607–11.

CAUDILL, WILLIAM. *The Psychiatric Hospital as a Small Society*. Cambridge: Harvard University Press, 1958.

GLASS, A. J. "Psychotherapy in the Combat Zone," in *Symposium on Stress*. Washington, D.C.: Army Medical Graduate School, 1953.

GOFFMAN, ERVING. "Characteristics of Total Institutions," in *Symposium on Preventive and Social Psychiatry*. Washington, D.C.: GPO, 1958.

RIDDELL, S. A. "The Therapeutic Efficacy of ECT," *Archives of General Psychiatry*, 8 (1963), 546.

11. TOMORROW'S POSSIBILITIES

LURIA, SALVADOR, and GUIDO PONTECORVO, reported by the Associated Press, April 7, 1963.

MULLER, H. J. "Human Evolution by Voluntary Choice of Germ Plasm," *Science*, 134 (1961), 643–49.